Guide to ownership, operation and maintenance of building services

CIBSE

The Chartered Institution of Building Services Engineers
222 Balham High Road, London SW12 9BS

Registered charity number 278104

ISBN 1 903287 05 7

Typeset by J Wilson

Printed in Great Britain by Black Bear Press Ltd, Cambridge

Foreword

Operation and maintenance of building services have been the Cinderellas of the building services industry for too long. They are now emerging as areas that require high levels of competence in a variety of taxing disciplines including: management of resources and risk, numerical and analytical capability, system redundancy assessment and probability theory.

These skills are also key elements in the property and estate operators' armour when demonstrating diligent management of the services which govern the environment in which we all live and work. Failure to maintain these services could result in contravention of health and safety or other legislation, reduced plant life, and risk of plant breakdown that affect business and staff performance.

With the advent of Private Finance Initiatives and Public Private Partnerships the importance of assessing the whole life costs associated with operating and maintaining a building which will be used for 30 years or more are becoming more widely appreciated. Many design decisions are being driven by the maintenance provider who will have this long-term responsibility.

This Guide is a continuation of the work of the CIBSE Maintenance Task Group and will be a valuable tool for those involved in the operation and maintenance of building services. It will also be an important source of reference for designers, manufacturers, installers and professional advisers. The hard work which went into its production demonstrates the importance that CIBSE attaches to these activities and the long-term commitment of CIBSE to this area.

Richard John
Chief Executive, CIBSE

Maintenance Task Group

J H Armstrong Chairman (Ove Arup & Partners)
R Clark (Commtech Group)
P Cottam (George S Hall)
P H Day (engineering consultant)
S Higgins (Winton Environmental Services)
D Howard (Watson & Sole Associates Ltd)
S Hunter (Dalkia)
R Jeeves (Imperial College of Science, Technology and Medicine)
I J Kelly (Lorne Stewart plc)
G Macefield (Defence Estates, Ministry of Defence)
R Nanayakkara (Building Services Research and Information Association)
D R O'Bryan (ASTAM GBC Consultancy)
R J Oughton
G Prudence
J J Rose (Ove Arup & Partners)
M Samuel
M H Smith (Building Services Research and Information Association)

Principal authors and acknowledgements

Section 1: Introduction
J H Armstrong (Ove Arup & Partners)

Section 2: Guidance for building services designers
M Samuel; R J Oughton; G Prudence

Section 3: Types of maintenance techniques and their applications
J H Armstrong (Ove Arup & Partners)

Section 4: Maintenance contracts
J J Rose (Ove Arup & Partners)

Section 5: Maintenance strategy and control
R Nanayakkara (Building Services Research and Information Association); R J Oughton

Section 6: Energy efficiency and maintenance
R J Oughton

Section 7: Plant service frequencies
R J Oughton

Acknowledgement: Safety Assessment Federation

Section 8: Heating, ventilating and air conditioning controls
R J Oughton

Section 9: Commissioning and testing
R Clark (Commtech Group)

Section 10: Handover procedures
T de Saulles (Building Services Research and Information Association)

Section 11: Operation and maintenance manuals
D Howard (Watson & Sole Associates Ltd)

Section 12: Risk assessment procedures
R Jeeves (Imperial College of Science, Technology and Medicine)

Section 13: Owning and operating costs
M H Smith (Building Services Research and Information Association)

Section 14: Economic life factors
P H Day (engineering consultant)

Acknowledgements: ABS Consulting; American Society of Heating, Refrigerating and Air-Conditioning Engineers; Building Services Research and Information Association; Caradon Trend; E-Squared Ltd; Heating, Ventilating and Air Conditioning Manufacturers Association (HEVAC); Krammer & Co; Land Securities Properties Ltd; Metropolitan Police Service Property Services Department Surveying and Engineering Division

Section 15: Maintenance audits
J H Armstrong (Ove Arup & Partners)

Section 16: Condition surveys
D R O'Bryan (ASTAM GBC Consultancy)

Section 17: Health and safety
S Higgins (Winton Environmental Services)

Section 18: The Construction (Design and Management) Regulations
R J Oughton

Section 19: Training
I J Kelly (Lorne Stewart plc)

CIBSE Co-ordinating Editors
K J Butcher; J David; R Yarham

Contract Editor
J Wilson

CIBSE Managing Editor
J Balian

Note from the publisher

This publication is primarily intended to provide guidance to those responsible for the design, installation, commissioning, operation and maintenance of building services. It is not intended to be exhaustive or definitive and it will be necessary for users of the guidance given to exercise their own professional judgement when deciding whether to abide by or depart from it.

Contents

1 Introduction

Engineers provide the internal environmental conditions that enable business processes to function at an optimum level while providing comfort conditions for occupants to achieve their maximum performance potential. The CIBSE motto is 'For the greater comfort of mankind'. The engineering services that provide this comfort need to be properly operated and maintained throughout their lifespan, which could extend to more than 30 years, to ensure that they continue to perform efficiently and viably.

This guidance is a continuation of work by the CIBSE Maintenance Task Group and is intended for the benefit of all those involved in the operation and maintenance of engineering services. The work follows on from previous publications, but principally Technical Memoranda TM17: *Building services maintenance management*(1).

The Task Group has tried to avoid duplicating information that is available elsewhere. Where information already exists, the reader is provided with a comprehensive reference rather than repeating the work of others.

The intention has been to identify current good practice and address topics of particular interest and relevance to those involved at all levels in engineering services maintenance. This includes designers, manufacturers, installers, maintainers, building owners, occupiers and operators, professional advisers and specialist providers. It is not expected that the reader will read the publication from cover to cover; rather that it will be used for reference and guidance as needs arise.

Maintenance of engineering services within the UK represents an annual business value conservatively estimated at some £2 billion. Maintenance is not the most glamorous aspect of engineering, and much of it is focused on preventing failure rather than creating something tangible. It is, however, becoming more analytical and numerically biased, including dealing with probabilities, management of resources, determining redundancy within systems and minimising risk.

This document is intended to raise maintenance into a sharper focus by helping building and property operators to become more aware of their responsibilities and duties. It will also help services designers to appreciate their role in providing installations that are safe, economic to maintain and operate, and capable of giving satisfactory performance over their full lifespan.

1.1 Scope and structure

The scope of each section of this Guide is summarised as follows:

— Section 2: *Guidance for building services designers* is particularly aimed at designers and identifies the areas that need to be taken into account from the earliest concept stage. Clients should also read the section as it emphasises matters that will need to be resolved and may need their commitment. Trouble-free use of the engineering services is a key objective of any property operator both in terms of economic, reliable performance and ensuring that legislation is complied with. The needs of the client are also discussed and the importance is emphasised of the designer fully understanding what the client expects to achieve.

— Section 3: *Types of maintenance technique and their applications*. Some of the techniques of maintenance have become complex and sophisticated, although opportunities for applying the full range within engineering services are often limited. This section gives an overview of the techniques to provide a general introduction and basic understanding of terminology and application.

— Section 4: *Maintenance contracts* looks at the contractual aspects of maintenance, covering types of contract, their content, legal details that influence which option to select, and how occupiers and property operators can ensure that the contract intent is being achieved.

— Section 5: *Maintenance strategy and control*. The maintenance strategy influences design decisions and therefore needs to be established before the start of detailed design. When the property and its services become fully operational, the maintenance strategy must be implemented and any revisions carefully assessed to determine the impact of any such changes on original design decisions. The section discusses this and the ongoing control of maintenance.

— Section 6: *Energy efficiency and maintenance* provides outline guidance on energy efficiency aspects of operating and maintaining. Readers should also refer to the CIBSE Guide F: *Energy efficiency in buildings*(2).

— Section 7: *Plant service frequencies*. The provision of regular servicing and maintenance will sustain the operating efficiency and prolong the effective life of the engineering plant. The section covers optimising the frequency, sources of detailed work schedules, statutory requirements and adjusting the frequency of attendance.

— Section 8: *Heating, ventilating and air conditioning controls*. The performance of any engineering installation will be directly related to the equipment that regulates and controls its operation. Section 8 provides a source of reference and guidance to this specialist area.

— Section 9: *Commissioning and testing*. Immediately following installation, a crucial stage is commissioning and testing; this ensures that the design intent is, or can be, achieved in practice. Procedures that need to be implemented for this to be successful are described.

— Section 10: *Handover procedures* addresses the handover of a fully functional, completed installation to the client. It identifies the point when the client accepts responsibility for security, insurance, operation and maintenance, and other contractual obligations triggered at that time. Also listed is information to be passed to the client and which forms part of the Health and Safety File.

— Section 11: *Operation and maintenance manuals*. Having put the services into operation, a key element towards long-term satisfactory performance is the availability of detailed and comprehensive operation and maintenance information. The importance of having this information has been reinforced by *The Construction (Design and Management) Regulations 1994*[3]. Information on the content, preparation and updating of the documentation is provided.

— Section 12: *Risk assessment procedures*. Part of any system design, installation and operation is the acknowledgement that there will be areas of risk, extending up to the final disposal stage. This is addressed, and the section includes a comprehensive assessment of how different risk activities relate to the risk categories of business, design, operation and disposal.

— Section 13: *Owning and operating costs* gives a detailed introduction to all aspects of cost management including types of cost data, bench marking, levels of information, cost prediction, budget control and investment appraisal.

— Section 14: *Economic life factors*. Possibly the most frequent question related to engineering plant and equipment is 'how long will this last?' or 'how long should this last?' The answers will depend on criteria such as the standard of maintenance, the severity of use and the degree of reliability required. Section 14 provides guidance and includes a comprehensive table of plant and equipment with details of life expectancies.

— Section 15: *Maintenance audits*. Having accepted the installation, produced a maintenance contract, agreed service frequencies and identified the full cost of ownership, the property operator or occupier may require that the performance of the maintenance provider is assessed. Section 15 shows a standard approach for this using objective criteria that, for example, can give a year-on-year comparison.

— Section 16: *Condition surveys*. At any time during the life of a property it can be useful to assess the condition of the building or its engineering services. The section covers the types of survey techniques including thermal imaging and methods of recording information.

— Section 17: *Health and safety* considers the relationship between the internal environment of a building, the health, safety and welfare of its occupants, and how the engineering services influence these factors. The guidance concentrates on air quality and thermal conditions, but also covers other aspects of occupant comfort.

— Section 18: *The Construction (Design and Management) Regulations* have extensive effects on maintenance work, although the Regulations need to be applied within the constraint of being reasonably practicable. Terminology and implications are reviewed.

— Section 19: *Training*. It is essential to ensure that maintenance engineers keep their skills up to date, continue to be aware of safety and health matters, develop individuals to maximum potential and help promote participation, ownership and belonging in a job that can be remote from the direct employer. Section 19 provides comprehensive information, including identification of needs, budgets, methods of provision and certification.

Given the potential interest of this document to all involved in building operation and maintenance, it is difficult to define the expected readership. Table 1.1 gives a general indication of where particular readers may find information most of value.

Table 1.1 Guide to relevance of sections

Readership	Section
Property owners, occupiers and operators	All sections
Designers	2, 3, 6–11, 13, 14, 17
Installers	3, 5, 6–11, 14, 18
Manufacturers	2, 3, 5–9, 11, 14, 18
Commissioning engineers	2, 6, 8–10, 17, 18
Maintenance providers/specialists	All sections
Professional advisers	All sections

References

1 *Building services maintenance management* CIBSE Technical Memoranda TM17 (London: Chartered Institution of Building Services Engineers) (1994)

2 *Energy efficiency in buildings* CIBSE Guide F (London: Chartered Institution of Building Services Engineers) (1998)

3 *The Construction (Design and Management) Regulations 1994* Statutory Instrument 1994 No. 3140 (London: The Stationery Office) (1994)

2 Guidance for building services designers

Contents

Summary

This section is primarily aimed at building services designers, but contains information of interest to all those involved in the management, installation, commissioning, operation and maintenance of engineering services within buildings.

It outlines the wide variety of aspects that designers should take into account when preparing their designs and highlights those issues that should be considered to ensure that a building services installation can be practically installed, efficiently maintained and will meet the client's written and implied aspirations in the short-, medium- and long-term.

The section does not cover the normally accepted tasks of preparing calculations and drawings of the building services designs; these are identified in the CIBSE Guides.

A client's exact requirements with respect to the operation and maintenance of engineering services may vary but the primary interest in almost every case will be to achieve trouble-free usage of the accommodation or premises. While there will be a general acceptance that engineering services need to be operated there will also be an expectation that such operation is within the scope of trained staff and will not require a proliferation of specialists. Similarly, clients will not expect the maintenance demands to infringe unduly on their usage of the premises.

Operating costs will typically be understood to include energy, maintenance and replacing minor plant items, with major plant replacement programmed and budgeted for separately. Client attitudes to running costs, however, may be more varied. At one end of the spectrum, a client may view running costs as being marginal when assessed against accommodation costs and staff wages, and simply accepts operating and maintenance expenditure. At the other end of the spectrum, a client may challenge even modest running costs in order to keep these under continuing review and to seek cost-effective means of improving efficiency and reducing expenditure.

The environmental impact of a building and its engineering services is another area where client attitudes may vary significantly. The attitude of some clients may be simply to ensure that they stay on 'the right side of the law'. Others may be committed to a formal environmental policy which could include third-party assessment and certification[1–4].

The use of the Building Research Establishment Environmental Assessment Method (BREEAM)[5–7] offers a comparative and quantitative means of assessing environmental aspects of particular design features.

2.1 Designers' responsibilities

In addition to the general responsibilities of designers to consider all aspects of the installation, there is a specific obligation under health and safety legislation and *The Construction (Design and Management) Regulations 1994*[8] (CDM Regulations) to ensure that the designs can be safely installed and maintained, and to identify areas of abnormal risk related to these activities. Section 18 deals with the duties and responsibilities under this legislation.

Designers have a key role in the performance of building services systems as a whole and, whether dealing with the overall concept design for large systems or preparing detailed drawings for a small part of an overall system, they should begin by addressing a range of questions which may include those given in Table 2.1. It is the responsibility of the designer to be aware of these aspects and to ensure that the installation meets its objectives.

The wide range of design responsibilities requires the design engineer to have a sound understanding of other construction disciplines and to be aware of the potential benefits of sharing ideas with other specialists. Wherever possible, designers should aim to present their proposals to installers, commissioning specialists and maintenance engineers, and to seek their input at an early stage before design proposals become too entrenched. This could help to facilitate later stages of the development and implementation of the design.

Appendix 2.A1 provides a design guide to maintainable buildings and could be used as a checklist to ensure that each stage and item is identified and addressed.

Table 2.1 Typical questions to be addressed by designers

Task	Question
Briefing	Do I clearly understand my role and responsibility for the installation? Do I really know what the client wants and what the brief is? Have I examined all the options? What redundancy is required (i.e. what standby facilities in case operating units fail)?
Materials	Have I thought about the materials to be used and their suitability and life expectancy? Have I selected materials that are safe to work with?
Installation and commissioning	Have I thought about how practical it is to install my designs? Do I have the necessary information to make that judgement? Will the installation be easy to commission? Can tolerances on design parameters be relaxed?
Operation and maintenance	Will my design work consistently and reliably to achieve the design objective under a wide variety of conditions? Can the installation be operated and maintained safely by personnel with normal skill levels?
Costs	Have I established the client's requirements in respect of: — first costs? — operating costs (including energy and maintenance)?

2.2 Advising and guiding the client

A client may seek advice and guidance on operation and maintenance aspects as outlined above or on related matters at any stage of the design process. In responding to such requests, building services designers should bear in mind the particular requirements and interests of the client and ensure that full account is taken of these.

In presenting the required guidance the designer should:

- use simple, straightforward language and terminology
- offer options for action wherever possible and outline disadvantages as well as advantages
- recommend a favoured option and state reasons for this choice
- provide indicative costings, both capital and running, for each favoured option.

2.3 Clients' requirements

2.3.1 Establishing the requirements

It is important for engineering services designers to ensure that they fully understand a client's requirements at an early stage of the design. In principle, the requirements should be relatively easy to define but most clients will have a limited understanding of operation and maintenance matters. This makes it important for designers to develop a detailed understanding in conjunction with the client and to ensure that all aspects are clarified at an appropriate stage of the design development (see appendix 2.A1). Where this is not achieved, there may be a subsequent need for design changes with adverse effects on both the programme and costs.

An effective means of targeting and clarifying client requirements is the use of a questionnaire. Clearly, the questionnaire needs to be particular to the project but certain core questions will be generally applicable. These may include, but not be limited to, those listed in Table 2.2. However, designers should develop their own in-house questionnaires or checklists geared to the way they operate their design procedures. These approaches will help to ensure a more purposeful approach to particular design development.

As with all documentation, user feedback is essential to ensure that the questionnaire or checklist remains relevant and fully effective. The content of such documentation should, therefore, be reviewed regularly, account being taken of previous experience.

In addition to establishing client understanding of and attitudes to operation and maintenance matters, building services engineers should acquaint themselves with the level of understanding by other members in the design team. In some instances it may be necessary for the building services engineer to take the lead in such matters on behalf of the team.

2.3.2 The brief

The key to success in any designer's activity is to understand the brief fully. Designers should not assume that they know the client's brief through either previous experience or knowledge of similar projects; they should interrogate the client and any representatives in an organised way. This can be carried out by a series of meetings or by a questionnaire (e.g. as Table 2.2). At a later stage it is essential to explain the completed engineering designs fully and clearly to the client and to ensure that the designs meet the requirements and aspirations.

Where there are design options that balance capital cost against life expectancy, running costs, maintenance costs and reliability, these should be carefully analysed so that the client has the opportunity to consider these issues and contribute to decisions on the options.

If the brief is not defined by the client, the designer should clearly outline a brief and explain the assumptions and the design parameters to the client and obtain the client's agreement (preferably with a formal agreement).

This particularly applies to the degree of redundancy associated with the various engineering elements of a scheme. It is for the client, not the designer, to decide the amount of standby capacity, the redundancy built into systems and the acceptability of likely rectification times in the event of failure. Designers, however, have a duty of care to advise the client of these decisions.

2.3.3 Specifying materials and components

The selection of systems and choice of equipment are as important as the basic calculations required in designing the system. The true test of a designer's ability is whether, ultimately, the systems and installation meet the client's brief and not simply whether the calculations are correct.

Designers must consider the suitability and life expectancy of materials being proposed in the light of the client's brief. The solution, for example, in a retail outlet where life expectation may be five years could be substantially different to an office development where lease and dilapidation requirements may stretch over 20 years. Clear guidance on these matters is important and, where appropriate, designers should carry out whole-life-costing studies.

The reliability of systems is only as good as the weakest part. Designers must be careful, therefore, to avoid specifying or allowing minor elements to be used that could have an adverse effect on the overall system performance.

The safety implications of materials and components is relevant both in the short and the long-term and designers should carry out their duties under the CDM Regulations[(8)] with care and diligence to ensure that any potential hazards or risks are identified and controlled (see section 18). This analysis should include any intrinsic or environmental dangers the designer is aware of together with any risks associated with installation of systems and any safety issues associated with maintenance. Under the CDM Regulations, the responsibility lies clearly with the

Table 2.2 Establishing the client's requirements

	Core questions to be asked
1	Is the client to be the building user? If not, is the building user known?
2	Does the client wish to operate on a total facilities management basis? If so, what are the responsibilities of each design discipline within the overall strategy?
3	Does the client have a maintenance policy?
4	Will the client employ a maintenance engineer/premises manager/facilities manager?
5	Will the maintenance engineer/workforce be in-house or by contract?
6	Does the client have a maintenance budget in mind?
7	Will the engineering services be operated (*a*) continuously? (*b*) intermittently for a 5-day week multi-shift operation? (*c*) intermittently for a 5-day week single-shift operation? (*d*) using other operational patterns?
8	What would be the feasible/preferred timing for routine servicing or monitoring attention on daily, weekly, monthly and quarterly bases (e.g. time of day; day of week; etc.)?
9	What would be the most demanding response time for emergency servicing in event of breakdown? To what parts of the building or services installation would this apply?
10	Is total contract maintenance to be applied to any plant items or parts of the building engineering services installations (i.e. where a contractor takes responsibility for the operation, maintenance and programmed replacement of plant or systems for a projected period of time)?
11	Is any part of the building required to be kept free from entry by maintenance personnel?
12	Does the client have preconceived views of economic life of plant and equipment? What is the investment programme for eventual plant replacement? (See sections 13 and 14)
13	Ascertain any preferred (or not preferred) manufacturers or suppliers.
14	Does the client intend to establish and maintain an asset register for plant and equipment items? (Design data schedules can take account of this and be compiled in an appropriate format.)
15	Ascertain client in-house policies or requirements and the level of client understanding of : (*a*) health and safety (*b*) environmental considerations (*c*) quality (*d*) refrigerants (*e*) water hygiene (*f*) energy efficiency (*g*) other aspects.

building services designer to ensure that the designs can be safely installed and maintained.

Where designers are encouraged to test the market, seek alternatives or write a performance specification, they should ensure that their requirements are properly specified and carefully detailed. This is essential to allow the materials offered by the installation contractor to be checked to ensure that they meet the performance specification, and do not cause dangers or difficulties which have not previously been considered. It is the designer's responsibility to ensure that the installation contractor has sufficient information to make an informed choice when alternatives are sought.

2.4 Installation

Engineering systems are an important part of the overall construction process and must be practical to install. The buildability of the installation and its maintainability should be considered fully by designers when preparing the outline and detailed designs as improvements are much simpler to implement at this stage. For instance, the equipment should be safely accessible and special tools or access platforms provided as necessary to ensure ease of access.

It is important that designers ask for, and obtain, information on decisions being taken on other constructional elements during the design process to ensure that the services design can be installed. Questions to be asked include:

— What is the type of structure?

— Are holes for services distribution systems to be pre-cut or formed *in situ*?

— How are items to be suspended from the structure?

— What is the permissible floor loading of the plant rooms?

— How is the equipment to be hoisted into position?

— Is there a site restraint on dimensions or weight?

— What are the delivery times?

— When is the equipment required on site in the construction process?

— Are the procurement lead times sufficient?

Designers need to resolve all these and many other issues at the specification stage. It is also important that the designed and specified installation is robust and will operate under the variety of conditions likely to be experienced during its operational life.

2.5 Design parameters

Building services designers have the responsibility to ensure that equipment and systems are capable of being operated in accordance with the design parameters and can be efficiently and safely maintained. As part of this, the written procedures provided to fulfil operation and maintenance requirements should be easily understandable and achievable.

Designers should also ensure that, either by specification or written recommendation, they set out general requirements for maintenance of their installation: this may be by reference to recommended standards or procedures set out in this guide and in other publications, such as the HVCA's standard maintenance specifications[(9)], to ensure that all important maintenance issues are fully considered. The preparation of particular, detailed maintenance procedures may be a separate responsibility.

In many instances, the designer's involvement with operation and maintenance does not extend beyond specifying and reviewing the content of operation and maintenance manuals for delivery to the client at handover. With the advent of the CDM Regulations[(8)], the content of these manuals forms part of the Health and Safety File for the project, the content of which is covered in principle by the approved code of practice[(10)]; see also section 18. The actual content of the manual will depend on the specification (usually prepared by the designer).

In most instances, the maintenance manual is not suitable as a basis for equitable, competitive tendering for an operation and/or maintenance service. In tendering, every effort must be made to ensure comparability of offers; for this reason, tenders need to be based on precise and definitive details of the maintenance procedures to be applied and their frequency. It is equally important for a maintenance specification to define the standard of technician or craftsman required to undertake the work as well as outlining some form of bench mark to cover the quality of the work carried out.

2.6 First-year operation and maintenance requirements

In the first year of usage of a new installation it is typical contractual practice to require installers, as a form of warranty of their work, to be formally responsible for any equipment, component or operational defects that may arise or become apparent. While designers are not directly implicated in this liability, their professional duty of care usually leads to an involvement in some way. This may be limited to identifying the true cause of any problem and providing an independent opinion on the apportionment of responsibility for a defect. In the case of more fundamental defects, the designer's input may entail a review of the design itself and, in extreme cases, the recommendation of design changes.

Details of all such defects should be fed back to the design team for formal review. This approach helps designers to work towards a 'right first time' approach and to filter out plant, equipment or design features that could lead to potential problems.

It is stressed that the contractual or warranty responsibilities for defects in the first 12 months after formal completion have nothing to do with, and do not include responsibilities for, routine maintenance.

It should also be noted that the need for maintenance attention does not lessen because the installation is new. Indeed, it may be argued that the need for maintenance attention during the running-in period is greater than under normal circumstances.

A possible option for first-year operation and maintenance is to enter into a short-term (12 month) contract with the installer. This question is more of a contractual than a design nature but designers should be prepared to outline the pros and cons of the option to the client. Where this course is contemplated, it is important for the designer/specifier to arrange for first-year operation/maintenance to form part of the actual installation tender; this ensures true competitiveness for both elements and the overall package.

This approach has the advantage that responsibility for first-year defects and for routine operation and maintenance are vested in the same organisation. In addition, there may be advantage to be gained from the knowledge of the installation held by the installer's organisation. It is not uncommon, however, for liaison between the maintenance and installation divisions of an organisation to be limited so that any potential benefit may not apply in practice.

In the event of a defect arising where the first-year operation and maintenance service is provided by an organisation independent of the installer, there is scope for the installer to argue that maintenance attention (or lack of it) was contributory to the problem. Therefore, this could be deemed to invalidate the installer's warranty. For this argument to be acceptable, it would be necessary to demonstrate that the applied operation and maintenance techniques were not in accordance with the instruction manual provided and that the installation did suffer damage as a direct result of this. Conclusive demonstration, one way or the other, may be difficult.

2.7 CDM Regulations

Requirements of the CDM Regulations[8] are dealt with in section 18. An example of design decisions that could reduce risks to safety and health in maintenance functions would be to change the material used in a component to make it lighter and easier to handle (e.g. aluminium or plastics in lieu of cast iron). The selection by the designer of paints and finishes, adhesives, lubricants and similar materials should also be based on the careful consideration of safety.

References

1 *BS EN ISO 14001: 1996: Environmental management systems. Specification with guidance for use* (London: British Standards Institution) (1996)

2 *BS ISO 14004: 1996: Environmental management systems. General guidelines on principles, systems and supporting techniques* (London: British Standards Institution) (1996)

3 *BS EN ISO 14005: Environmental assessment of sites and entities* (London: British Standards Institution) (in preparation)

4 *BS EN ISO 14010: 1996: Guidelines for environmental auditing. General principles* (London: British Standards Institution) (1996)

5 *Building Research Establishment Environmental Assessment Method for Offices* BREEAM 98 (Garston: Building Research Establishment) (1998)

6 *Building Research Establishment Environmental Assessment Method for New Offices* BREEAM version 1/93 (Garston: Building Research Establishment) (1993)

7 *Building Research Establishment Environmental Assessment Method for New Superstores and Supermarkets* BREEAM version 2/91 (Garston: Building Research Establishment) (1991)

8 *The Construction (Design and Management) Regulations 1994* Statutory Instrument 1994 No. 3140 (London: The Stationery Office) (1994)

9 *Standard maintenance specification for mechanical services in buildings: Volume 1: Heating and pipework systems* HVCA **SMG90** (1990); *Volume 2: Ventilating and air conditioning* HVCA **SMG90b** (1991); *Volume 3: Control, energy and building management systems* HVCA **SMG90c** (1992); *Volume 4: Ancillaries, plumbing and sewerage* HVCA **SMG90d** (1992); *Volume 5: Electrics in buildings* HVCA **SMG90e** (London: Heating and Ventilating Contractors Association) (dates as indicated)

10 *Managing construction for health and safety: Construction (Design and Management) Regulations 1994 Approved code of practice* HSE **L54** (London: Health and Safety Executive) (1995)

Appendix 2.A1: Design guide to maintainable buildings

Consider options

Development budget

Development expertise → Building requirement/inception ← Development budget

Traditional architect-led construction team?

Speculative building or user driven or user requirement → Formation of project team including:
Project manager
Client representative
Architect
Design engineers
Quantity surveyors and consultants

Outline design brief formulated

Set up communication channels
Total commitment

1. Feasibility

Location of building	
Weather/climate	
Air/noise quality required	
Microclimate for broad assessment of A/C requirements and possible options	
Effect of weather on services equipment located outdoors	
Electrical/heat/cooling load (estimates)	
Types of systems and equipment available	
Possible services (essential)	
Reliability/availability requirements	
Associated maintenance requirements	
Cost implications	
Services life cycle/building lifespan	
Buildability of services	
Adaptability	
Local issues affecting service designs (e.g. transport/access to site)	
Feedback from previous buildings of same type	
Sick building syndrome considerations	
Highlight/weed out rogue options	
Consider maintenance resources required and integrate with user preference (i.e. on-site/remote, in-house/contracted)	
Report containing possible options, main services requirements, maintenance, reliability and costs to design team	
Health and safety plan	

2. Outline proposals

Minimise services requirement	
Simplify those deemed necessary	
Highlight essential services	
Incorporate changes to feasibility brief	
Future use of building, change of use, service capacity	
Plantroom locations	
Focus on daylight, max/min temperatures	
Specific space/weight requirements	
Plantroom/riser sizes	
Services required/specialists?	
Business systems, IT/telephones etc.	
Shell and core — fit out?	
Integration of services	
Specific use of floor/spaces	
Lighting and power requirements	
Fresh air requirements	
Water system options and consumption	
Control systems for services	
Risk analysis/contingencies	
Waste removal/disposal	
Legislation/statutory requirements	
Access to plant areas and systems	
Closer investigation of possible services	
Reliability/availability, maintainability	
Standardisation of services	
Assist architect in glazing choice (possible manufacturers/spares)	
Possible maintenance resource/costs	
Are sufficient skills available to maintain equipment which is deemed necessary?	
Facilities support on board with proposals to date?	
Keep it simple	

3. System design

Verify outline proposal report and integrate with all design team members	
Ensure facilities representative included (if not previously appointed on design team)	
Firm up envisaged maintenance regime, initiate selection of staff/contractor if possible (i.e. management organisation)	
Design systems to user agreed specification:	
• HV electrical distribution	
• LV system	
• Generators	
• UPS system	
• IT power distribution	
• Lighting systems	
• Lifts/escalators	
• Cooling systems	
• Heating systems	
• Water systems/public health	
• Air systems	
• Acoustic provision	
• Handling systems	
• Fuel/energy systems	
• Fire systems	
• Building management system	
• Occupant controls?	
Reconsider possible maintenance implications	
Reconsider:	
• Reliability/availability	
• Maintainability	
• Access	
• Manufacturers types available	
• Availability of spares/services	
• Alternatives considered	
• Compliance of systems with legislation	
• Integration/coordination between systems and other project disciplines	
• Identification of plant	
Access for maintenance/replacement	
O&M documentation requirements	
Standardisation of services	
Life cycle costing	
Risk assessments/contingencies	
Commissionability/retests	
Avoid overspecification	
Report to design team/client	

Early appointment of management commissioning team to test commissionability of evolving services design

Constant feedback to client or known specifier of options, reliability, maintainability and direct/long-term/alternative costs.

Continuous awareness to provide an energy efficient, environmentally considered solution

Multidisciplined design/ project team?

Design consultant or contractors?

Client and occupier

Operations and maintenance/facilities expertise: interface communication or member of design team?

Use of building, occupants (number and times)?
How will it be handed over/operated?
What form of O&M documentation will be required?
(Accuracy is important:
a poor or loose brief can be disastrous later in project)

4. Detailed design

Review options to date	
Include feedback from client	
Detail design/specification of all services of system design	
Practical application of:	
• Reliability	
• Maintainability	
• Stand-by/duplication	
• Access	
• Standardisation	
Maintenance regime:	
• On site	
• Remote	
• In-house	
• Contract	
Specialist contractors requirement	
Operational competency required	
Legislation and testing possible	
Availability of service	
Manufacturers/types	
Are components available?	
Avoid 'specials'	
Will design conditions always be met? How often will they not? What is inconvenience/cost?	
Frequency/convenience of plantroom access	
'Design out' problems and excess maintenance	
Outline O&M documentation	
• Planned preventive maintenance	
• Breakdown maintenance	
• Corrective maintenance	
• Condition-based maintenance	
Computerised maintenance required?	
Isolation points — test facilities	
Coordination of services and disciplines for best overall solutions	
Specific service levels identified	
Future expansion	
Plant renewal implications	
Complete services life costs	
Keep it simple!	
Final solutions report to project team	
Is client fully aware of what will he/she be getting and overall costings?	

5. Production information

Tender/contract information	
Specifications	
Precise O&M documents	
Form of handover (guide etc)	
Bill of quantities	
Work stages/CDM Regs	
Method of installation	
Commissioning specification and programme	
Expected results of commissioning?	
Training requirements and staff available for training	
O&M regime identified	
Control and retention of site information to O&M documents	
Operational procedures	
Spares requirement	
Highlight associated legislation, codes of practice and guides	
Clarify performance service levels	
Full support of facilities team	
Identify O&M cost separately	
Adequate retention specified?	
Penalties for poor maintenance	
Complete tender documents	

6. Tender

Tender evaluation	
Presentations to ensure contractors fully committed to specification including service level, maintainability, energy and environmental requirements	

7. Pre-construction

Method statements to ensure compliance with CDM Regulations and all other requirements	

8. Construction

Ensure installation is as design drawings to include valves, drain points and access	
Manufacturers specified are actually used	
Adequate on-site control	
Commissioning team on site to see installation process	
Allow adequate time for commissioning	
Facilities/operational staff presence on site	
Draft O&M documentation handed over early in construction	

9. Commissioning

Full test of operations to design spec	
Maintainability	
All site documentation controlled and offered at handover	
Facilities team involved with commissioning	
CBM/vibration techniques used to check equipment to standards and specification	
Early completion of final handover documentation	
'Stave off' occupation until thoroughly commissioned	
All defects remedied	
Facilities team training complete	
Equipment labelling adequate	

10. Handover

Legislative items in place	
Maintenance regime in place	
O&M/Asset information, health & safety in place	
Minimal defects to clear	

11. Occupation

BMS 'fine tuned' over 1st year of building occupation	
The optimum, energy efficient building meeting user requirement	

Feedback occupation and experience, knowledge for benefit of future projects	

3 Types of maintenance techniques and their applications

Contents

Summary

The section outlines a series of items that can influence an organisation in establishing its maintenance policy. The management of maintenance is subdivided into 'technical' and 'control' elements, and the objectives of each are summarised.

The principal options for maintenance are discussed and the various types described together with some examples of prospective applications. Guidance is given on the establishment of a maintenance policy for an organisation and the choices of maintenance strategy open to the maintenance or facilities manager.

An algorithm is presented to help in deciding the optimum type of maintenance to apply to a particular installation and an example is given of the typical range of services that can be covered by maintenance.

The engineering plant and equipment used in buildings serve a variety of purposes. They provide the environmental conditions which make occupants comfortable (e.g. heating, ventilation, air conditioning and lighting), communication facilities (e.g. telephones, staff location systems and data transmission equipment), emergency standby power supplies (batteries and generators) and basic necessities such as water supplies. Once such services are installed in the building, they require continuing attention to ensure that they operate correctly and economically and that they are available for use when required.

As an example, most buildings are provided with heat by boiler plant which converts the potential energy in fuel to realisable heat in the building, using a combustion process. The efficiency of this conversion will depend on the condition of the plant involved. If it is properly adjusted and monitored, there will be a commensurate saving in energy use stemming from a high level of operational efficiency. Inadequate or no attention could mean that the plant is unsafe to operate.

Such adjustment and monitoring, and other activities that ensure plant is available and can perform its required function, are in essence the maintenance requirements.

Many reasons can be put forward to justify maintenance being carried out, such as to:

— comply with the law, in particular health and safety requirements

— comply with the terms of occupation (e.g. lease)

— protect the value of the property as an investment

— maximise plant utilisation and minimise non-availability of the engineering services

— provide a service to the building occupants

— ensure a safe, healthy environment for the building occupants

— ensure energy is used efficiently

— project and help protect a corporate image

— fulfil a business need.

3.1 Management of maintenance

Management of maintenance can comprise more than the control of activities associated with each item of equipment and can be addressed broadly under the headings of 'technical' and 'control'.

The technical content includes determining what plant is to be maintained, how and when; identifying problems and diagnosing causes; monitoring effects; preparing and analysing records and technical information; initiating procedures to cope with situations before they arise; and ensuring that the chosen techniques are achieving the required results.

The control element is aimed at providing the required technical service at minimum expense, and can involve management of labour, spares and equipment to match the workload; locating where work is required; organising transport; setting priorities; and coordinating action. It can extend to setting budgets, monitoring expenditure, identifying high maintenance cost plant and collecting information to form a basis for decision making.

Effective maintenance management minimises the costs associated with the non-availability of an engineering service. It should be recognised that in addition to enabling the engineering services to be available when required, maintenance is vital to ensure that the services retain their value as assets within the building.

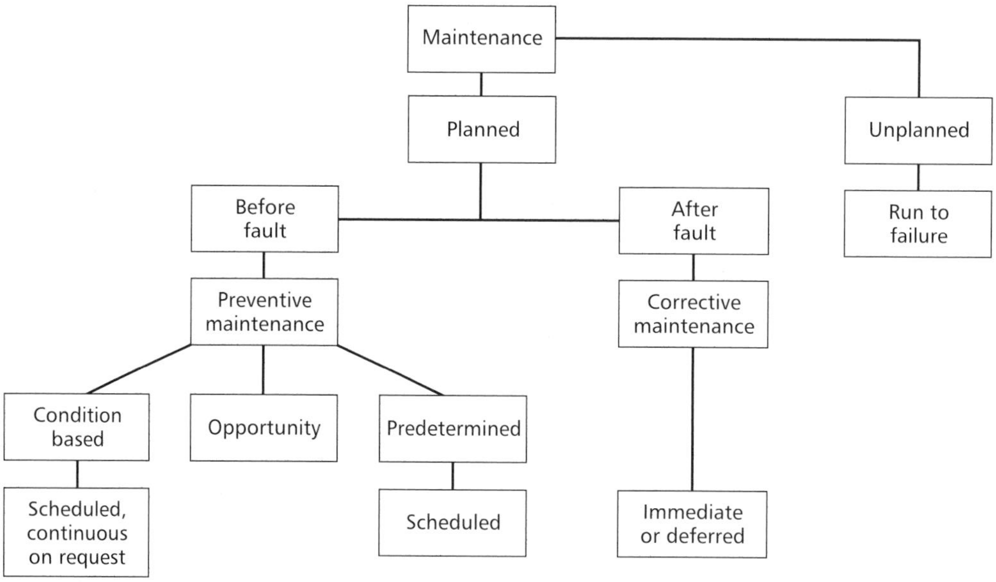

Figure 3.1 Overview of planned and unplanned maintenance

3.2 Options

Maintenance of engineering services plant within buildings has traditionally been carried out in a variety of ways by a variety of people. For buildings with relatively simple engineering services — e.g. small shops and commercial offices, small schools and industrial units — the building operator may view the services installations in much the same way as those for domestic premises. Similar options exist.

For example, no routine maintenance may be done, with plant and equipment being left until it breaks down, on the assumption that adequate resources can be called on for action when such an event occurs. Typical organisations that might be used are the local gas, electricity and water supply companies, and local contractors offering a similar service. Large organisations such as local authorities may have some form of agreement, either formal or informal, with local contractors to respond to such breakdown situations at agreed labour rates. Supervision of such work may be by an individual specifically appointed for this by the building operator, the local manager of the property or at the discretion of the contractor.

A second option is to make a more formal arrangement for a particular property with a maintenance contractor. Examples could be a service and maintenance agreement with the local gas supply company for gas-fired equipment or a regular testing of the electrical installation by an electricity supply company. Such services will also be offered by dedicated maintenance contractors.

A third option is to employ a maintenance labour force which routinely inspects and maintains all the engineering services. For building operators with small to medium-sized property, the cost of employing such personnel cannot usually be justified — where such staff are employed they would probably be expected to carry out additional tasks, such as portering and message services or waste disposal. They may be regarded as 'general handymen', able to turn a hand to most routine problems but calling on specialist advice when non-routine problems occur.

In larger buildings such as major office complexes, department stores, hospitals and hotels, where there can be a variety of engineering services plant perhaps providing essential services, a more formal maintenance structure tends to be adopted. Two principal options exist: to use directly employed labour or to let the work to a maintenance contractor. In any particular case, reasons exist for adopting either course. Further information about the comparison of options is available in CIBSE Technical Memoranda TM17 *Building services maintenance management*[1].

As the size of building or property estate increases, so does the justification for employing a specialist to be responsible for maintaining the engineering services. Directly employed labour and maintenance contractors may sub-let work on specialist equipment where they have insufficiently detailed expertise.

3.3 Types of maintenance

Maintenance can be divided into two broad categories: unplanned and planned. Figure 3.1 provides an overview.

In unplanned maintenance there is no organised arrangement to follow and everything is carried out as a reaction to a situation, possibly resulting in prolonged breakdowns, frustration and loss of control. Unplanned maintenance suggests that the building operator takes no responsibilities for the failure of the engineering services and the inevitable consequences. It is not recommended as a technique to be adopted and is, therefore, not considered further.

Planned maintenance is organised, controlled and follows a recognisable procedure. It can take several forms, such as:

(*a*) Preventive maintenance: carried out at predetermined intervals or corresponding to prescribed criteria and intended to reduce the probability of failure.

(*b*) Corrective maintenance: work done once a fault has occurred to restore plant to normal operation; this approach would be subject to prior agreement by the building user that this is an acceptable basis for maintenance.

(*c*) Immediate maintenance: necessitated by unforeseen breakdown or damage and needing to be put in hand immediately.

(*d*) Scheduled maintenance: preventive maintenance carried out to predetermined intervals, number of operations, hours run etc. The Heating and Ventilating Contractors Association (HVCA) in conjunction with CIBSE has published a series of standard maintenance specifications[2] for the majority of building services plant and equipment. These provide a useful source of reference for maintenance requirements and typical frequencies.

(*e*) Opportunity maintenance: work done as and when possible within the limits of operational demand.

(*f*) Design-out maintenance: other forms of maintenance may be inappropriate, therefore maintenance needs are designed-out to achieve the required level of reliability.

(*g*) Condition-based maintenance: work initiated by trends highlighted by routine or continuous monitoring of the condition of plant, such as general performance or specific parameters (e.g. bearing vibration and motor-winding temperature).

(*h*) Run to failure: the consequences are such that plant can be safely and cost effectively run to destruction without serious loss of service. This may assume there is a standby unit that will automatically operate on failure of the duty unit.

Whichever maintenance plan is adopted, it is likely to consist of a mixture of these methods. It needs to start with an assessment of what is effective followed by a decision as to what is desirable and a consideration of the resources available in terms of labour, materials and facilities; together, these should provide a rational basis for preparing a programme of planned maintenance.

Condition-based maintenance is initiated by monitoring the condition of plant. This is becoming more applicable to building services as the techniques gain understanding and credibility, the equipment becomes simpler and cheaper, and clients become more demanding in terms of plant reliability.

The concept is that a parameter can be established which gives a good indication of plant condition and also reflects the likely mode of failure. By monitoring this parameter, the required timing and type of maintenance can be determined. Monitoring can be assessed by establishing trends over time to identify marked departures from the normal, or by condition checking where readings are compared with established parameters for the particular item of plant or equipment on a 'go/no go' basis.

Various techniques are available, generally requiring routine plant inspections. These include: visual inspections; thermography; oil wear analysis; ferrography, temperature, pressure, speed and flow monitoring; vibration analysis; bearing shock measurement; voltage, current, power, frequency monitoring; and non-destructive testing. Plant that could justify condition monitoring would typically be:

— expensive to maintain
— expensive to replace if run to failure
— failure could lead to high consequential costs
— failure could lead to an unacceptable situation (creating a safety hazard or causing an essential building function, such as a data processing, to cease to operate)
— critical to the overall building operation.

'Designing-out' may appear an ideal solution but should be considered only where other options are not available. For example, where health and safety considerations, operational requirements, reliability demands or even building location dictate that other maintenance requirements are not viable. The use of designing-out can put a major responsibility on the design engineer. In most building services applications it is unlikely to be encountered as the only option, but the client should be aware of it and ensure that this is clearly defined in the

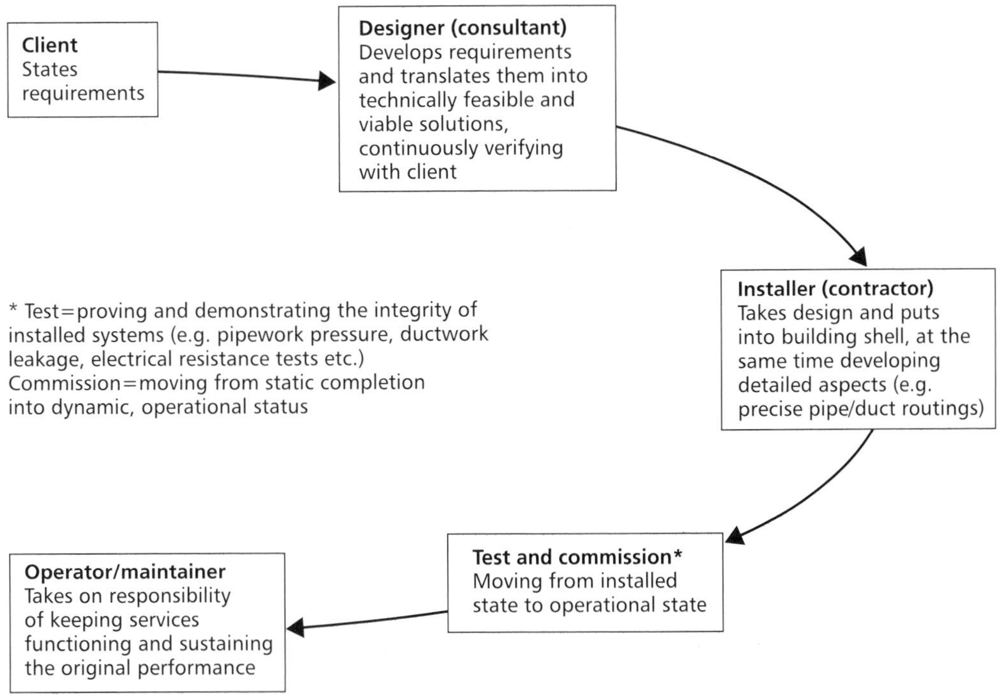

Figure 3.2 The traditional manner in which a building services project progresses

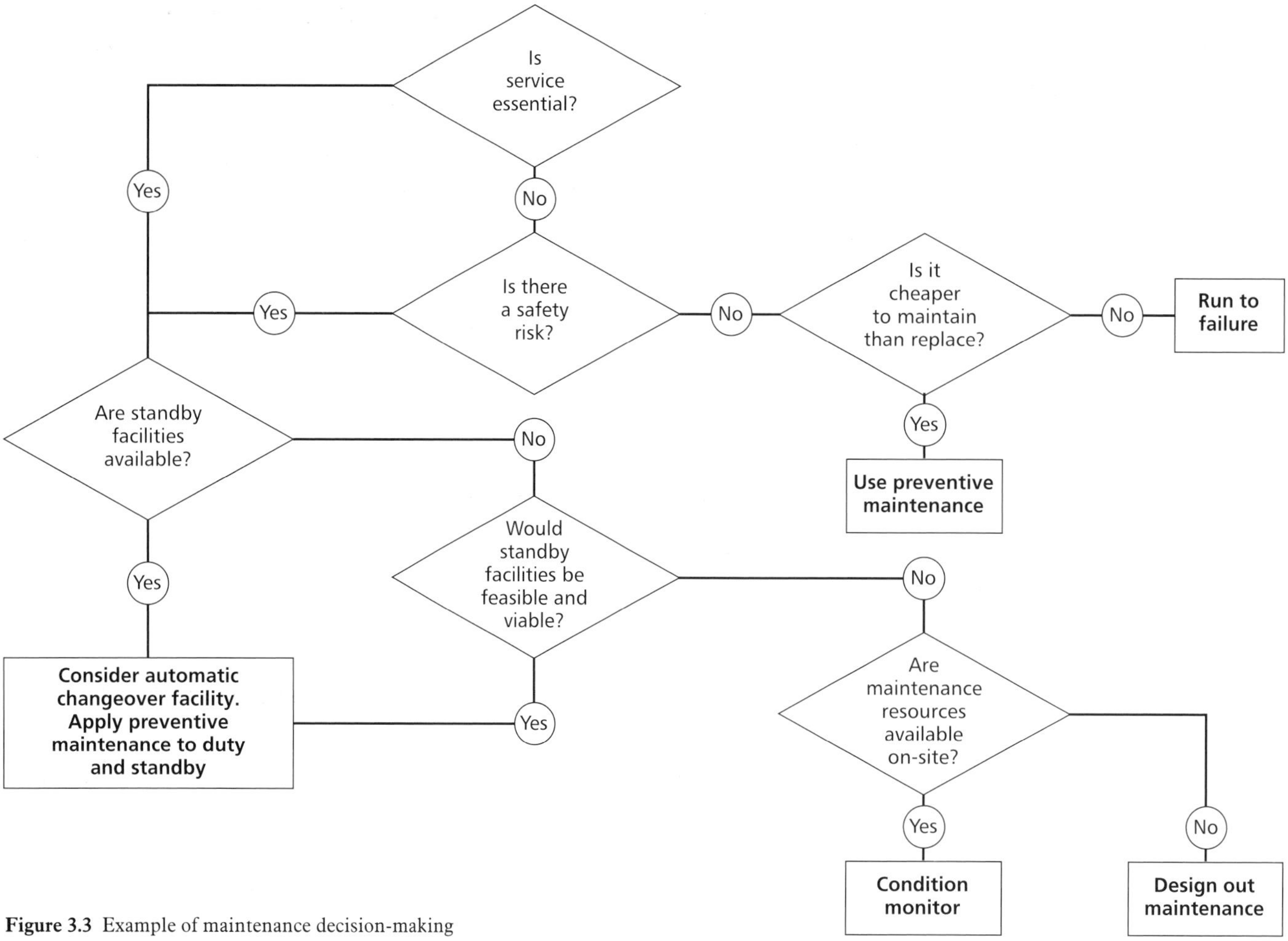

Figure 3.3 Example of maintenance decision-making

brief if considered appropriate. This requirement may have a significant cost implication, but is far more readily addressed at the design stage than during or after installation.

A technique increasingly being adopted in the process industry entails relating the operational requirements of specific plant to known or recorded reliability information. This can allow more cost effective use to be made of maintenance resources, particularly labour. It can be implemented by methodically listing plant items and using group analyses (the group being drawn from plant and maintenance operatives, supervisors and managers) to review and improve the maintenance regime with ongoing monitoring of the results of changes to meet the aim of continuing improvement.

3.4 Establishing a maintenance policy

The traditional manner in which a building services project progresses is shown in Figure 3.2. This figure demonstrates how the earliest concepts of a project can affect its eventual outcome as they become translated from concept to reality. For the final scheme to be successful and capable of proper and adequate operation and maintenance, due allowance needs to be made at the earliest stages, ideally in the form of a policy statement by the client when briefing the design consultant. The design stage can then take full account of this policy. If a maintenance policy is not available, perhaps because the client does not have the necessary expertise, it should be established at an early design stage by the designer recommending a series of suitable options to the client and agreeing the optimum approach with the client.

During installation, the specified maintenance policy can ensure that appropriate and safe means of access and isolation are provided, proper means of identification and test facilities are available, and information such as maintenance requirements and suitable spare parts lists is on hand. The testing and commissioning stages should ensure that the installation can be operated and maintained effectively from handover in line with the original maintenance policy (see also sections 9 and 10).

The maintenance policy for any installation is likely to be unique, but many of the variables are likely to apply generally. The following questions are intended to help in the formulation of a policy:

(*a*) What are the implications of failure?

(*b*) How is this plant likely to fail?

(*c*) What is the probability of failure?

(*d*) Are standby facilities available?

(*e*) What level of use is envisaged?

(*f*) What type of maintenance is envisaged?

(*g*) What level of technical expertise will be available, and how will it be organised?

(*h*) Will spares be available on site?

(*i*) Can equipment be purchased or rented locally?

(*j*) Can a standard of maintenance be stated?

(*k*) Will all necessary documentation be provided?

(*l*) What financial resources will be available for maintenance?

The answers to these questions are also likely to affect how subsequent maintenance decisions are taken, but as more detailed stages are reached beyond the initial design brief the types of decisions needing to be taken may not always relate directly to the policy statement. A structured approach at these stages can be beneficial by ensuring that a consistent and logical method is followed. Figure 3.3 shows how such a structured consideration could be applied to the design process and could also influence maintenance planning.

3.5 Choice of maintenance strategy

A building operator needs to determine the most appropriate choice of maintenance procedures when a building is eventually handed over and put into full operational use. The strategy may closely follow the original maintenance policy established by the client in conjunction with the designer but, as the project progresses to completion, other factors may need to be considered. The usage pattern of any functioning building is likely to be continually changing and the maintenance procedures will need to adapt to suit the circumstances.

For example, in the early years it may be appropriate to keep an installation close to its original condition but, as wear becomes more pronounced and the needs of the occupants change and technology improves, there is likely to be an increasing demand for extensive replacement and refurbishment. In many cases it may be left to the person responsible for carrying out maintenance to recommend a course of action, perhaps solely on the grounds of cost without fully appreciating the implications of alternatives.

Whichever approach is finally adopted, it should take account of anticipated future requirements of a building and its services, the current physical performance and functional suitability of plant, proposed changes of use (particularly where they affect plant and services), statutory and legal requirements, and any standards of maintenance specified by the building operator.

Table 3.1 sets out an example of how this could be approached. It shows part of a list of the services in a building and the analysis to establish the detailed maintenance requirements. To be effective, such a procedure needs to be kept up-to-date — perhaps on a five-yearly basis for a relatively new property with little change of use but more frequently where services are approaching the end of their economic life or the building use is changing frequently.

3.6 Main principles of a planned maintenance system

The following checklist itemises the details that need to be established for a planned maintenance system:

(*a*) items to be maintained

(*b*) maintenance policy appropriate to each item

(*c*) labour required

(*d*) material resources required

(*e*) when the work is to be done

(*f*) how frequently the work is to be done

(*g*) how the maintenance system will be administered

(*h*) how the results will be analysed and monitored.

3.7 Typical range of maintenance services

An example of the range of services carried out by a direct labour organisation or maintenance contractor is set out below; additions may be appropriate to meet particular requirements.

(*a*) routine inspection and maintenance of engineering plant

(*b*) planned lamp replacement

(*c*) five-yearly electrical inspection

(*d*) portable appliance testing

(*e*) monitoring of plumbing and water services operation (for legionellosis control)

(*f*) inspection and operation of high-voltage electric installation

(*g*) first line response to emergencies and pre-agreed critical alarms (response time agreed with client)

(*h*) ensuring compliance with statutory requirements for services installations

(*i*) provision and control of on-site engineering stores

(*j*) purchase of engineering plant and equipment (consumable spares and materials, client requested items, replacement of minor and major plant)

(*k*) installation of engineering plant and equipment (minor items including response to client requests and major capital plant)

(*l*) energy management by

- (*i*) ensuring efficient plant operation
- (*ii*) purchase and, where appropriate, storage of fuel

(*m*) supervision and control of specialist contractors

(*n*) inspection, compliance testing and monitoring of fire systems and equipment

(*o*) trouble-shooting.

Table 3.1 Reviewing maintenance policy

Building type: Hotel   Location: Brighton

Engineering plant or service	Minimum statutory requirement	Implication of failure	Age (years at 2000)	Estimated remaining life (years)	Assessed current reliability	Relative energy use	Notes
Gas-fired cast iron boilers serving low-temperature hot water radiators and hot water services calorifiers. All pumps have on-line standby with manual changeover	Gas Safety Regulations annual inspection	100% loss of building function	15	15	Good if inspected six-monthly	90% of total gas consumption of building	Energy consumption below average for type of property. Good service by local contractor (24 hour call out). Boiler efficiency 80%
Lifts (2)	Six-monthly inspection	Virtual loss of 75% building function	2	28	Good	3% of total electricity consumption of building	Statutory inspection essential; current arrangement with *XYZ* insurance satisfactory; no service contract required at present
Electric power installation	Five-yearly inspection	100% loss of building function; no lights or heating, no standby generator	25	5	Fair: localised breakdowns of subcircuits		Last inspection report indicated deteriorating situation. Inspect every two years using local electrical contractor; ensure 24 hour standby. Hotel management to isolate sections in emergency — training needed
Kitchen		Minimal: can use catering facilities in hotel next door (planned arrangement)	Generally >20	0	Poor	High: inefficient and badly managed	Imminent plan to amalgamate catering and do away with this kitchen. No maintenance except make safe on breakdown

References

1 *Building services maintenance management* CIBSE Technical Memoranda **TM17** (London: Chartered Institution of Building Services Engineers) (1994)

2 *Standard maintenance specification for mechanical services in buildings: Volume 1: Heating and pipework systems* HVCA **SMG90** (1990); *Volume 2: Ventilating and air conditioning* HVCA **SMG90b** (1991); *Volume 3: Control, energy and building management systems* HVCA **SMG90c** (1992); *Volume 4: Ancillaries, plumbing and sewerage* HVCA **SMG90d** (1992); *Volume 5: Electrics in buildings* HVCA **SMG90e** (London: Heating and Ventilating Contractors Association) (dates as indicated)

Bibliography

BS 3811: 1993: Glossary of maintenance terms in terotechnology (London: British Standards Institution) (1993)

BS 3843: Guide to terotechnology (economic management of assets); Part 1: 1992: Introduction to terotechnology; Part 2: 1992: Introduction to the techniques and applications; Part 3: 1992: Guide to the available techniques (London: British Standards Institution) (dates as indicated)

Building Research Establishment Environmental Assessment Method for Offices BREEAM 98 (Garston: Building Research Establishment) (1998)

Building Research Establishment Environmental Assessment Method for New Offices BREEAM version 1/93 (Garston: Building Research Establishment) (1993)

Building Research Establishment Environmental Assessment Method for New Superstores and Supermarkets BREEAM version 2/91 (Garston: Building Research Establishment) (1991)

Armstrong J H *Operations and maintenance manuals for building services* BSRIA Application Guide **AG1/87.1** (Bracknell: Building Services Research and Information Association) (1990)

Nanayakkara R and Smith M H *Operation and maintenance audits* BSRIA Technical Note **TN24/97** (Bracknell: Building Services Research and Information Association) (1997)

de Saulles T *Handover information for building services* BSRIA Technical Note **TN15/95** (Bracknell: Building Services Research and Information Association) (1995)

Building services maintenance BSRIA Reading Guide **RG6/95** (Bracknell: Building Services Research and Information Association) (1995)

Smith M H and Tate A *Maintenance programme set-up* BSRIA Application Guide **AG1/98** (Bracknell: Building Services Research and Information Association) (1998)

Building services maintenance management CIBSE Technical Memoranda **TM17** (London: Chartered Institution of Building Services Engineers) (1994)

Health, safety and welfare in the built environment CIBSE Technical Memoranda **TM20** (London: Chartered Institution of Building Services Engineers) (1995)

The Construction (Design and Management) Regulations 1994 Statutory Instrument 1994 No. 3140 (London: The Stationery Office) (1994)

The Control of Substances Hazardous to Health (COSHH) Regulations 1999 Statutory Instrument 1999 No. 437 (London: The Stationery Office) (1999)

The Electricity at Work Regulations 1989 Statutory Instrument 1989 No. 635 (London: The Stationery Office) (1989)

4 Maintenance contracts

Contents

Summary

General guidance is given on the essential elements of a contract, differentiating between contracts 'under hand' and 'under seal' and outlining details of particular statutes that directly affect contracts.

The major components of contract documentation which provide the basis for competitive tendering and the 'rules' for the management of a contract are described, with particular reference to specialist contractors.

A comprehensive breakdown is provided of the types of maintenance contract available, the elements of each being outlined.

Guidance is given on the invitation and analysis of tenders for maintenance contracts, the initiation of a contract and the various articles of a contract that offer protection to the client. These need to be included in the documentation but may present difficulties in applying in practice. Advice on the management of a contract is outlined and a sample questionnaire for the prequalification of prospective tenderers is provided.

Building services engineers are involved with contracts and contractors in virtually every aspect of their normal work. Their involvement, however, may be predominately with contracts for the installation of plant and systems and often with one particular form of contract (e.g. JCT 80[1]). Generally, the engineer produces the design, specification and drawings for the work, with a quantity surveyor or project manager responsible for the contract conditions and other additions to form the total contract documentation. In many cases, the engineer may not be involved with the finalisation of a legally binding contract, including the steps to putting a contract in place, and consequently may not be fully familiar with some contractual details.

There is currently no generally accepted standard form of maintenance contract and this makes the engineer's task difficult. An example of a standard form is the Department of Environment's *General conditions of contract for maintenance*[2]. This covers the operation, repair and maintenance of mechanical and electrical plant where the contractor is responsible for maintaining equipment in running order.

When providing the complete maintenance contract documentation, special effort should be put into recognising the legal aspects of the task and engaging the support of relevant advisers where necessary. There is nothing special about the terms associated with maintenance contracts compared with other types of contract, nor the way that they are put in place. The key aspect to bear in mind is that they are service related.

Installation contracts are for a specific and relatively short period of time, to provide a tangible end product. They have a clear finish point where the parties have discharged their contractual obligations. In fact, time can be made 'of the essence' in such contracts.

Maintenance contracts have a specific duration but no easily measurable or deliverable product, unless the absence of breakdowns is considered a product. There is no point at which the parties can say that the service is finished or complete, apart from at the end of the contract. The need for the service continues.

It is important, therefore, to recognise the different requirement of the scope of maintenance work compared with an installation project and how satisfactory performance will be measured. These factors then need to be put into a context that can be included in the contractual framework.

CIBSE Technical Memoranda TM17 *Building services maintenance management*[3] contains detailed guidance on the technical and management content of maintenance contracts. BSRIA Applications Guide AG4/89.2 *Maintenance contracts for building services*[4] also provides comprehensive coverage of the subject with particular attention to contractual clauses and the tendering and monitoring processes. This section draws summary headings from these documents and extends the guidance on the contract and procedural matters.

4.1 Contract details

4.1.1 Essence of a contract

The intention in this section is to alert engineers to the ease with which a legal agreement can be formed, and to warn of the obligations that may unintentionally arise.

A contract may be formed when three basic steps have occurred:

— there is the intention to create a legal relationship (i.e. there is no contract if the parties are conspiring to commit a crime) and that litigation will arise in the event of default

— an offer has been made by the contractor and it has been accepted without qualification by the client

— consideration has been agreed (some form of benefit or payment).

In addition, the following must be true:

— possibility of performance: the contracted obligations are capable of being performed

— contractual capacity: neither party is of a type of whom advantage might be taken (e.g. minors, insane persons)

— genuineness of consent: neither party gave consent to the contract by fraud, deceit, duress or misrepresentation, either deliberate or otherwise; also the person giving the consent was duly authorised to do so.

Each of these steps may occur almost without the parties realising. Contracts can be established on a verbal basis, but it is always preferable to make arrangements in writing. Verbal agreements cannot be easily verified at a later date, whereas the written word is reproducible.

4.1.2 Confirmation of contracts

A contractor may make an offer in writing that may be accepted verbally. The verbal acceptance may, in reality, be in the form 'yes but...'. Unfortunately, the 'but' may not be obvious or not thought to be that important and certainly, being verbal, will not have been recorded. The contract will therefore be based upon the written evidence of the contractor's offer.

A formal acceptance frequently comprises the issue of a company 'standard order', often with company conditions on the back. In the event of a dispute, these company conditions may be interpreted as a counter offer, invalidating the contractor's bid. If confirming an otherwise variable estimate (compared with a fixed quotation), the issue of such an order consolidates that estimate into a fixed price and cannot be revised later when it is recognised that the estimate was higher than need be.

4.1.3 'Under hand' and 'under seal'

Where contracts are in writing, they may be 'under hand' or 'under seal'. The reference to 'under hand' merely means a signed contract. 'Under seal' refers to signatures upon a document bearing a seal or stamp. With contracts 'under hand' there is a limitation of liability for a period of six years whereas with 'under seal' the period extends to 12 years. The seal ensures that the extended liability period is recognised by both parties at the time of signing. It therefore follows that if a client requires a contract 'under seal' the required process must be followed at the time of signing. Due to the ongoing nature of a maintenance service, the question of 'under hand' or 'under seal' may not arise.

Signatures are not essential to form a contract. The carrying out of the service can be taken to prove that the agreement exists, particularly if a payment has been made to the contractor. The contract will be based upon the last exchange of understanding between the partners. This allows counter offers to replace the tender document requirements or other means of explaining the client's needs. Counter offers may consist of the contractor's response to the tender inquiry in a letter where the body of the letter contains qualifying comments and the standard terms and conditions are on the back.

It is important to be aware of the standing of these exchanges. If both parties carry out the intentions of their agreement and both are content with the outcome, it is unlikely that the terms and standing of the contract will be examined. When things go wrong and the contract is brought into play to determine the way forward, the situation changes. If legal opinion is sought, it is then that the client and professional adviser who prepared the contract realise the true quality or otherwise of the contract put in place. This is usually too late and the eventual apportionment of blame and cost may not be placed in the way intended by the person drafting the original contract.

Those producing contract documents should recognise their own limitations, particularly in understanding the law and arriving at a contract agreement. This is not to say that a lawyer is needed on every occasion; standard forms of contract are relatively safe to use provided that they are not heavily amended and the procedures are properly understood and followed. Where contract conditions are specially written, or amendments are made to existing contract terms, the client should be advised to obtain legal advice.

4.1.4 Legislation

Two Acts of Parliament directly affect maintenance contracts: the *Unfair Contract Terms Act 1977* [5] and the *Supply of Goods and Services Act 1982* [6]. The former allows the courts to apply 'tests of reasonableness' to any exclusion clauses and prevents exclusion of liability for death or personal injury resulting from negligence. The latter implies quality into contracts for supply and 'fitness for purpose'. This places maintenance contracts on a par with those governed by the *Sale of Goods Act 1979* [7], which requires that:

— where no specific time has been agreed before the contract was made, the work must be completed within a reasonable time

— if no specific charge was agreed before the contract was made, the price must be a reasonable one

— the work must be performed with reasonable care and skill.

If new legislation comes into force during a contract period and results in extra expenditure by the contractor, particularly if related to the execution of the works rather than a general requirement upon the contractor, the client must be reasonably expected to pay some or all of the extra cost.

4.2 Components of contract documents

4.3.1 Content

Generally, a set of contract documentation will contain the following sections:

(*a*) contract conditions, which deal with issues such as:

- definitions
- payment
- the service required, in principle only
- commencement and duration of the contract
- how the contract might be terminated
- insurances

(*b*) schedules to the contract, which include job-related details such as the job specification, its scope and demarcations.

More details are given in CIBSE Technical Memoranda TM17[3] and BSRIA Applications Guide AG4/89.2[4].

The definitions section should be considered carefully, as it will create the meaning of any word and make it specific to the contract. Other interpretations will no longer apply.

It would seem reasonable for the complexity of contracts to reflect the complexity of the service, and in particular that simple services have simple contracts. If neither party understands the meaning of the contract terms, the best that can happen is that they become subsidiary to getting the work done. The worst that can happen is that both parties waste their energies in arguing over what was meant by the original writer of the clauses, sometimes to the extent where progress of the works becomes secondary.

It is essential to recognise that the contract conditions will be worded in general terms and should not be altered to become specific. The specific requirements will be detailed in the schedules referenced from within the contract conditions. For example, contract conditions may refer to the payment clauses ('The payments as stated at Schedule One') or 'The scope of work as detailed at Schedule Two'.

4.2.2 Scope of work

The scope of work schedule will be tailored for each project but will have particular headings:

- the service required within the price
- the type of maintenance regime
- hours of access for the contractor
- response times for call-outs
- quality of staff
- resident or visiting maintenance technicians.

More headings are listed in CIBSE Technical Memoranda TM17[3] and BSRIA Applications Guide AG4/89.2[4].

Typically the scope of work will make it clear whether any or all the following services are to be provided and how each will be paid for:

- operation of services
- maintenance only
- repair
- component or partial plant replacement
- total plant replacement
- call-out services
- record keeping and updating of as-fitted drawings
- energy monitoring and energy management
- budget planning
- small works.

4.2.3 Specialist contractors

The engineer will need to bear in mind whether a contract with a specialist contractor is to maintain a particular item of plant or a system, or for a more overall responsibility including multiple plant and systems (e.g. chillers, automatic controls, the building management system, fire alarms and lifts) and perhaps involving specialist sub-contractors. The basic concepts of assembling the documents do not change, but the service that can be expected will be different because it will be provided by another party.

Specialists normally fulfil their duties on a visiting basis and cannot be asked to operate plant in the day-to-day sense. They may require attendance from other personnel (e.g. the electrical technician that knows the building) to be able to work safely or to open work areas for access.

The schedules of work for specialist contractors will deal with other information such as asset registers, any drawings that may be worth including and any tasking required.

Responsibilities for health and safety, insurance inspections and legislative matters must also be made clear.

4.3 Types of contract

There are a variety of types of maintenance contract:

- service level agreements
- labour only
- inspection and maintenance
- planned preventive maintenance
- caretaker maintenance
- measured
- fully comprehensive
- comprehensive
- call-out only
- specialist services.

There are also different forms of financial agreement:

- fixed price with or without inflation or variation adjustments
- lump sum
- estimated price
- cost plus
- measured work
- competitive or negotiated.

The essential point is that the parties need to recognise exactly which type of contract they are entering and what the contract details and financial arrangements include and, more particularly, do not include. In practice it might be found that even a contract perceived as fully comprehensive with fixed annual payments may have extra costs, such as replacing major capital plant should it reach the end of its economic life during the contract period.

Whichever type of contract is chosen, the purpose, objectives and methods of measuring success must continue to be understood by all involved parties throughout the duration. Contract performance measurement by negative indicators — such as the number of breakdowns or the incidence of environmental conditions being outside agreed performance parameters — can inhibit success by creating adverse working relationships. The client must also be aware of the need for an adequate type of contract to be in place for the contractor to perform. If the intention of the contract is to care for plant and systems fully and to prolong their economic life, more than breakdown maintenance will be required.

The following paragraphs expand on the types of contract available and reflect the general interpretation of the maintenance industry. The effectiveness of the contract documentation for each type of contract is totally dependent upon the quality of the wording in the scope of works, the tailoring of the work content to the specific plant installed, understanding the client's requirements, and the successful implementation of the system design and installation.

4.3.1 Service level agreements

This is a contract where the duties are not laid down as a series of tasks but as performance standards. The contractor may use any method of achieving the defined services and performance standards (e.g. space temperature will be between 21 °C and 23 °C during all hours of occupancy).

4.3.2 Labour only

A purchaser may wish to avoid the complication of employing staff directly; under this type of contract the provision of labour including the skills and expertise required is the responsibility of the contractor. This may extend to site supervision but the purchaser is responsible for direction, supervision and control of the maintenance labour force.

4.3.3 Inspection and maintenance

A large number of contracts with specialist contractors are of this type. For a fixed sum, the contractor will undertake to visit a site and look at the item of plant to confirm if it is working correctly. If the plant is capable of having any maintenance carried out on it (such as topping up oil, filters checked etc.), this is also done. Any work of a more specific nature or any repair will have an extra cost associated with it. Thus for, say, £1000 per year a chiller specialist may visit a site four times, check that the chiller is operating and is performing as expected. Additional costs arising out of these inspections (e.g. subsequent repair work) can easily double the basic cost.

The choice of contractors should be heavily influenced by their experience and familiarity with the specific plant. Specialist plant manufacturers may be the most suitable supplier of this service as they will have access to spares and knowledge of the expected operational performance.

4.3.4 Planned preventive maintenance

Planned preventive maintenance (PPM) entails the contractor carrying out task-related maintenance work to an agreed plan with the intention that its proper completion will minimise the risk of loss of service from the plant and optimise its economic life. The detailed maintenance tasks may form part of the tender documentation or be provided by the contractor within its tender return. Both tend to be unrelated to a specific manufacturer of plant or installed systems. The tasking can be made site- and usage-specific. This could bring significant value to the contract for the purchaser by defining in detail the client's requirements, but is a more costly exercise than the use of standard tasking such as that published by the CIBSE/HVCA *Standard maintenance specification for mechanical services in buildings*[8].

4.3.5 Caretaker maintenance

Sometimes referred to as 'a watching brief' when applied to installations in unoccupied buildings, this is an undervalued and widely interpreted service.

In an empty building there is a value in looking after the building services in such a way that they will work and can be readily recommissioned when the building is re-occupied. The building insurer may also require that selected systems, such as fire detection and protection, are active and maintained to minimise the risk. Over long periods, because water is not being drawn off, it may become a breeding ground for bacteria, or water traps in drainage systems may dry out and release foul fumes into the space. The health and safety of security staff who may be resident in the building for 24 hours per day and of visiting surveyors and purchasers may need to be considered, not just for drinking water but emergency lighting and the maintenance of passenger lifts. Some plant may be suitable for 'mothballing' where the water systems may be drained or be treated to minimise deterioration. Basically, it should not be assumed that an unoccupied building requires no maintenance attendance.

4.3.6 Measured

Measured contracts are not very common due to the difficulty and cost of measuring the work. The measure may be by completion of tasks or, more often, by hours worked and materials used. A measured type contract could be the best way of starting a maintenance regime in a badly run down building in order to direct effort and cost most effectively. Once the installation has been assessed and brought to a known level of repair, a more traditional type of contract can be applied. The cost of the direction and measurement process can equal the cost of the measured work.

4.3.7 Fully comprehensive

A fully comprehensive contract covers the supply of labour, materials and any other necessary resources to manage the maintenance of the building services plant over an agreed period. Should plant items fail, they will be repaired or replaced as deemed appropriate by the contractor, at no additional cost to the client.

A fully comprehensive contract will need an appropriate term to ensure that the premiums taken for full plant replacement risk are likely to be called upon. To have a five-year plant replacement contract would appear to be more of an insurance than a business-based plan. Such a contract placed on a 15-year-old building would be a high risk to the contractor. It may also not be possible for the true condition of plant and systems to be determined before the price is agreed, leading to conflict regarding the basis of the contract where the actual requirements for plant replacement significantly exceed what may have been viewed as a reasonable competitive estimate.

4.3.8 Comprehensive

This is a variant of the fully comprehensive agreement that limits the liability of the contractor. For example, cover may include replacement of component parts up to a stated unit value (e.g. £1000) but exclude complete systems and major plant items (such as heating, boiler plant, air conditioning and chiller plant).

4.3.9 Call-out only

The contractor provides an agreed response service (e.g. to attend to the site and repair or make safe within four hours). The actual cost of attendance plus materials will be charged at an agreed rate when used. There may be a minimum attendance time charged, or a retainer cost for making this facility available.

4.3.10 Specialist services

Lifts, escalators, complex automatic controls, major refrigeration plant, fire alarm systems, security systems, uninterruptible power supplies and water treatment are all examples of specialist services within building services maintenance where particular expertise is required. This may be obtained through the main maintenance contractor who arranges subcontracts and incorporates their costs into the charge to the client, or the client may appoint the specialist services contractors directly.

4.3.11 Shared savings

With the range of services of a comprehensive agreement, it may be possible to identify opportunities for cost savings. These will directly benefit the client, but it may be advantageous to agree some form of sharing to provide an incentive to the contractor to identify cost savings to the client. Examples are:

- reducing the inspections on specific plant based on reliability gained from operational experience
- replacing capital plant at the end of its economic life with a high efficiency equivalent to give energy savings.

4.3.12 Private finance initiative (PFI)

Under a private finance initiative (PFI), major projects are let as a simple contract for the anticipated lifespan (e.g. 20 years) rather than considering the work in two stages (initial capital installation followed by ongoing operation, maintenance and repair). The PFI contractor will need to arrange the finance for the initial cost, put up the installation and be responsible for its maintenance and operation throughout the full contract term. The client is then committed to regular payments over the lifespan that will cover the initial capital cost and interest plus the subsequent ongoing costs.

PFI contracts allocate the risks for design, funding, installation and operation to those best able to manage them, leaving the client (or service user) to concentrate on core business activities. The concept is being applied particularly in the public sector to enable capital developments to take place. It also puts more onerous responsibilities on the development contractor who has to accept the risk of the ongoing viability of the installation over the full life of the contract.

A number of issues are raised under PFI. These include:

- performance measurement and facility availability
- a clearly defined brief for the installation and its requirements (the infrastructure specification), together with its stated purpose throughout its lifespan
- contract documentation and terminology to ensure full commitment and risk transfer by all parties for the duration of the contract
- how to predict plant life expectancy to make due allowance in the cost model (i.e. life cycle costs and major maintenance funds)
- protecting the value of the assets during the contract period (the assets may devolve back to the client at the end of this period).

4.4 Tender and award of maintenance contracts

Maintenance contracts can be placed in many ways varying from selecting one contractor and negotiating a contract with them to a complete formal selection, tendering and award procedure. The choice will be influenced by available time and the needs of the client. The tender process should reflect the duties placed upon the successful contractor.

A full formal procedure might include:

- prequalification of contractors to form a tender list
- the tender period
- site visit by the tenderers
- response to tenderers' queries
- receipt of sealed tender returns by a qualifying time and date
- tender opening procedure
- written tender analysis
- post-tender return interviews
- recommendations
- award
- contract document and signing
- start of contract meeting and site familiarisation
- acceptance and reporting period for sites incorporating full plant replacement contracts.

4.4.1 Prequalification

Prequalification is a process intended to ensure that tenderers are capable, suitable and competent for the work and to confirm that they will provide a tender price. Many different factors may be appropriate to allow a choice to be made, including the location of the contractor's office in relation to the site, the size of the company and the workforce (particularly those local to the site), basic hourly rates and management policies such as training, health and safety. Larger contractors may be unhappy about being on the same list as a small contractor for reasons of differing overheads or capabilities. The prequalification process should be designed to answer such criticisms.

Figure 4.1 shows a sample questionnaire for use in the prequalification process.The minimum selection criteria are:

(*a*) capability to supply the type of service required

(*b*) degree of previous experience in the specialisation required

(*c*) ability to provide the skills for the type and complexity of the activity required

(*d*) ability to provide the resources necessary to carry out the work wherever required

(*e*) economic aspects

(*f*) financial standing and/or availability of external financial support

(*g*) need for guarantees for performance over the time of the contract

(*h*) check of information provided by the supplier for accuracy

(*i*) competence of personnel (e.g. skills certifications, refrigerant handling, welding).

Tender lists need be no longer than five contractors. With only three contractors, the spread of prices may not help with tender evaluation. With more than five, it becomes uneconomic for the contractor to invest time in studying the particular needs. The likelihood of losing the bid is greater and thus the costs incurred will not be repaid. That cost will be put into the company overheads and must be recouped on future jobs won. Thus excessively long tender lists will be bad in two senses: the overall price of contracts will go up for no more return and the contractor's interest in pricing the tender accurately will be reduced.

4.4.2 Tender period

The tender period will influence the contractor's ability to price the tender. Too short a period and the information that it may need to seek from subcontractors may not be obtainable. Too long a period and the contractor will postpone dealing with the inquiry. Three or four weeks would appear appropriate for the average tender. Particularly large or complex tenders will need longer.

4.4.3 Site visits

A visit to the site by the contractor may be deemed essential and might be most appropriate at the middle of the tender period. Most maintenance contractors have sales and estimating departments who prepare their tenders. Many will involve the contract manager who would run the project in the bid preparation. A conducted site visit allows both the tenderer and the engineer to meet each other and helps to ensure a common understanding of the intended scope of the contract. The engineer can receive feedback on the specification and gain some insight into the contractor's thinking and interpretation. This can often allow clarifications to be circulated to all tenderers in good time during the tender period, promoting the chances of successful operation of the contract once awarded.

As a guide, a minimum of 1.5 hours is needed for a site visit and should encompass those aspects of the site that will exert the most influence on the contractor's price. Viewing the plant is obvious, but if access to occupied spaces or storage are potential problems, the site visit is a good opportunity to allow these issues to be aired. Individual visits for five contractors might take a full working day; a collective visit reduces the time and allows more opportunity to explore the details of the site.

Individual site visits for each contractor are costly for the engineer or client and may not achieve the intention of keeping the tender list private. Where subcontractors have been named in the tender documents, the tendering contractors will need to contact them for information. This may also result in the names of the tendering contractors being divulged.

4.4.4 Responses to contractors' queries

Responses to contractors' queries during the tender stage should be copied to the other tenderers to ensure equality of interpretation. (However, if a tenderer asks a specific question that would affect only its own bid, the sharing of this information may not be helpful or relevant.) Such questions will indicate how clear the wording is in the tender documentation. Responses need to be timely as they may affect the ability of the contractor to return a price and thus leave the engineer in a difficult position at tender evaluation stage.

4.4.5 Receipt of tenders and opening procedure

Some procurement groups require tenders to be returned in unmarked envelopes to avoid identifying the source and subsequent confidentiality issues. Franking machines which state the sender's name and courier labels tend to work against this. The tenders returned within the specified time limit should be opened at a formal session in the presence of a witness and the salient details recorded and signed by those present.

4.4.6 Tender analysis, interviews, recommendations, award

Tender prices should be analysed against an agreed set of criteria that will normally be determined when the tender documents are being prepared. This can include total tender price, labour costs (normal and premium rates), mark-up rates for materials and subcontractors, travel costs, ability to resource the work and understanding of the client's requirements.

Post tender, it can help to gain confidence in the potential contractors and resolve concerns by selecting a shortlist and then conducting interviews. The interviews should be conducted by the client and the professional adviser (if one is being used) and be based on a prepared framework and address such issues as:

— quality and skills of labour force
— programme of work
— responding to client's additional requirements
— client reporting procedure
— out-of-hours response
— training and health and safety policies
— track record.

Following the interviews and any further assessment of tenders which may be shown to be appropriate, the engineer and other professional advisers (such as the quantity surveyor) should be in a position to recommend the most favourable contractor to the client. Once decided, notification should be provided in writing. The unsuccessful tenders should also be advised and ideally given an opportunity of feedback.

4.4.7 Contract initiation

Once the successful contractor is selected and agreed by all parties, the contract start date needs to be confirmed. This allows the full contract documents based on the tender documentation, and any subsequent matters clarified during the tender process, to be produced.

The contractor should sign and date two copies for submission to the client, who also signs and dates them, retains one and issues the other to the contractor. It may be possible to arrange this at a formal session with both parties present. Such a meeting can also provide an opportunity to start the contract formally and to resolve outstanding issues and matters of concern, such as:

— security vetting of contractor's staff
— method of gaining access to building
— password procedures
— invoicing procedures
— contractor reporting process
— timetable for future meetings
— review of client requirements
— contractor review period to accept plant condition or report need for replacement or remedial works
— storage and workshop facilities.

4.5 Practical difficulties

Some issues addressed in maintenance documentation may not be familiar and may therefore be difficult to apply in practice. The following paragraphs deal with some of these and may assist the engineer to recognise other similar difficulties.

Writing a specification that describes what is needed can be the start of a long journey. If the person drafting the specification is well versed in what the marketplace can provide and can compile a specification that asks for exactly what the contractor normally and routinely does, receiving the price will be quick and the service will be properly and satisfactorily delivered. However, this is not always achieved.

4.5.1 Enforcing the contract

Getting someone to agree to enter into a contract is one thing; regulating the implementation of the contract and, where necessary, enforcing this is another matter. When a contractor fails to do something that is written into the specification, it is important to know what the contract allows. The more detailed the requirements at tender, the easier it is to discuss the difference between expectation and delivery. The contractor may have been asked to keep records of maintenance. If the record forms or examples of the forms had been included as part of the tender documentation, it would be easier to discuss departures from the specified requirements with the contractor and to make a decision to either accept the departure or take some action.

4.5.2 Manufacturer and installing contractor warranties

It is very difficult to obtain the benefit of these. It may seem simplistic but eventually it all comes down to money. For a new building, the owners assume and expect that for perhaps one year after handover any defect in the installation will be put right at no cost to them. This may

1 Name and address of maintenance contractor

....

....

....

2 General Information

2.1 Personnel

Total number of staff providing the maintenance service ....

Total number of technical staff providing the maintenance service ....

2.2 Company activity

What proportion of the total turnover of the organisation is that provided by the maintenance service?
(e.g. total company turnover £3 million, maintenance service turnover £1 million, proportion as % = 33%)

State proportion by value over past three years

Year	20.....	20.....	20.....
Proportion of turnover	......%	......%	......%

State value of maintenance service provided over past three years

Year	20.....	20.....	20.....
Value	£......	£......	£......

2.3 List current principal clients

....

....

....

2.4 Envisaged development of maintenance activities

....

....

....

2.5 Provide an organisation chart showing functions, staff numbers and interrelationships

3 Means of maintenance

3.1 What IT systems do you use?

....

....

3.2 Personnel

What are your normal working hours?

....

Do you divide work groups into teams? If so, how is this arranged?

....

....

3.3 What safety training is provided?

....

....

3.4 List the training and technical qualifications of staff providing the maintenance service

....

....

....

....

3.5 What is the method of travelling for mobile staff?

....

Figure 4.1 Sample questionnaire for use at prequalification stage for preliminary assessment of a maintenance contractor

3.6 How are telephone calls and other messaging systems handled and recorded?

....

....

3.7 Describe how standby duties and emergency call-outs are provided

....

....

4 Associated operations

4.1 Describe the size, location and facility for materials storage

....

....

4.2 Describe the type of stock you normally hold and how non-stocked items are obtained (including during emergency call-outs)

....

....

....

5 Administrative and commercial issues

5.1 List the extent of insurances in place

....

....

5.2 Do you participate in or are you a member of professional, trade or commercial institutions or organisations in the field of maintenance?

....

....

6 Methods and procedures

6.1 List your maintenance methods or procedures (e.g. planned maintenance programme, issuing process for follow-on-work)

....

....

6.2 Do you follow a quality assurance procedure?

....

6.3 Do you have a methodology for reviewing and improving procedures?

....

7 Safety

7.1 Do you have safety procedures in place? If so, describe their operation

....

....

....

7.2 Provide copies of the annual safety report for the past three years listing safety statistics, frequency of occurrence and gravity of incidents

Figure 4.1 *Continued*

be stated in the construction contract. Chillers or boilers installed early in a construction project may be five years old at project completion, and the manufacturer's warranty no longer valid.

For an extra premium the building operator might extend the warranty period, but has the manufacturer been given the opportunity to care for the product while it has been sitting dormant on site? If an extra premium has been paid to extend a warranty, who was it paid to and how far down the chain did the payment pass? Who is carrying the risk and what is the procedure for the presumed warranty holder to mobilise the warranty?

These are essential issues to be clear on when bringing warranties into a maintenance contract. The warranty may also state that appropriate maintenance must have been carried out for it to remain valid.

The construction warranty probably does not say how quickly the defect is to be put right. A maintenance contract may require a two-hour response to a breakdown, which is unlikely to be written into the warranty of a manufacturer or installing contractor.

The real cause of a failure or loss of service will be hard to determine and non-technical people will have to fall back on the contract to determine who will pay. An insurance similar to that used for domestic appliances might prove to be a less confrontational and more satisfactory approach.

4.5.3 Performance bonds

Performance bonds are another form of insurance against non-performance, but they are not common in maintenance contracts. A client may require a contractor to provide a guarantee to pay a specified sum of money to the client if a measurable or detectable event fails to happen. The contractor will go to a bank or insurance company and pay a premium to the bond provider on the understanding that the bond provider will pay the agreed sum to the client in the event of the contractor's default.

The most interesting aspect of a performance bond is whether all the parties are clear on the event that is to be the trigger for payment of the bond. If the trigger event is not clear, the bond may become worthless.

4.5.4 Collateral warranties

Most services are procured contractually between two parties. The providing party may use subcontractors or even sub-subcontractors. If a subcontractor defaults, the client body may have recourse only to the company it has contracted to. If the contractor ceases trading for any reason, there may be no contractual route to the subcontractors. Collateral warranties are warranties given to clients directly by subcontractors or by contractors to remote parties working on behalf of the client.

An insistence on collateral warranties can extend contract negotiations unacceptably. It can almost make a nonsense of the tender process if the details of the maintenance service being offered have been revised during negotiation. A sensible review of risk and benefit and alternative means of covering the risk may be worth greater consideration.

4.5.5 Parent company guarantees

Over a period of time, maintenance companies may change their names or ownership, or cease trading. Some advisers consider that a guarantee by the company's parent or owner to continue to provide the service in the event of the contracted company's demise gives some degree of protection.

In terms of the continuance of service, even if the contracting company has ceased trading the technicians with the site-specific knowledge and technical skills may still exist and be able to continue the service. Payments are usually in arrears for services so there may not be any financial loss unless the contract was on a fully comprehensive, full plant replacement basis. In which case, the benefit of replacement without cost and any associated premiums will be lost.

4.5.6 Disputes and their resolution

A contract is an agreement between two parties. If one party thinks that the other is not performing its part of the agreement, they have a dispute. Ideally they discuss it and find a way in which they can continue with the agreement, modify it by mutual consent to take account of the new factor or agree to terminate their arrangements. If they cannot achieve this by mutual agreement they need a third party, whose decision they are both prepared to accept, to consider the issues and report formally, recommending a solution.

At one time, the only third party was a judge whose opinion was obtained by going to court, i.e. litigation. This was seen to be an expensive way to settle a dispute and the concept of a qualified arbitrator was conceived. Events show that this route may be no less expensive and now the concept of adjudication has been introduced by the *Housing Grants, Construction and Regeneration Act*(9).

An alternative process being considered to resolve disputes is mediation, using an independent expert or mediation specialist where appropriate.

The inclusion in a contract of a specified means of settling a dispute means that this method must be used. However, the absence of a reference to this in contract does not preclude appropriate means being used.

4.5.7 Insurances

Insurances are always mentioned in the contract conditions. There are several types of insurance and the engineer should consider their relevance.

The absence of insurance or the inability to obtain it has other implications. Insurance against particular events is meant to provide recompense to the client or a third party: obtaining that recompense directly from a contractor will be more protracted than an insurance claim. However, requesting too high a level of insurance can be self-defeating. The insurance companies are prepared to underwrite a contractor's risk if they know the risk record for the particular circumstances. Hence, professional indemnity insurance may be expensive for a contractor whereas accidental damage may not, for similar sums of risk.

There are many different types of insurance. It is important to understand the types of insurance requested and offered in response. Also the recipient of the pay-out needs to be identified and how the level of insurance is set. If there are multiple insurances for the same event, and various companies could share the pay-out, there may be no worth in the final settlement to the client.

Typical insurances referred to in contracts are:

- employer's liability
- public liability
- damage to persons and property
- professional indemnity
- consequential loss including loss of profit
- fire.

There is also the question of plant insurance for unexpected events such as catastrophic boiler failure (note this does not provide cover for gradual degradation).

If the contractor is not insured, it does not mean that the contractor cannot be asked to pay for damage caused; it merely means that the contractor may not have the resources to pay.

Employer's liability refers to the liability the contractor has to its employees.

Damage to people and property is relatively straightforward. Most building owners are already insured through their own insurance for damage caused by contractors while on their premises. Many contractors can offer £1 million or even £2 million of damage cover, but if a client insists on more extensive cover, it may be easier to obtain this directly rather than seeking it from the contractor. It can be difficult and expensive for contractors to obtain more than £2 million of damage cover, and sums of, say, £10 million may be unobtainable. It should also be remembered that the client pays for the insurance in the end because it is an element of the contractor's price.

Professional indemnity refers to claims against the contractor in the event of faulty advice or design. In the past, contractors have not been asked for this form of insurance, but as they change their market position from contractors to design/build or providing more than maintenance services (e.g. energy management, small works design and project management), clients will expect such insurance. Depending on the levels of competence of their staff, maintenance contractors may have difficulty obtaining this type of insurance at acceptable rates.

Some consideration should be given to defining who the beneficiary of any insurance should be. The common assumption is that the beneficiary to the insurance will apply the funds to the reparation of the insured loss, but this does not necessarily follow. Insurance in joint names is often referred to, and proper advice should be sought and understood to ensure that the intention is achievable in practice.

Proof of insurance is essential. For professional indemnity insurance it will be necessary for the insurance to be in place at the time of the claim, which may be several years after the original appointment has concluded.

4.5.8 Damages

Liquidated and ascertained damages refer to the ability of the employer in the contract to recoup losses from the contractor (insured or not). Liquidated damages are where the employer has set a fixed sum to represent the loss it might suffer. In the event of a claim, it will not have to prove the loss but merely claim the agreed sum. Ascertained damages are where the loss must be proven. Such a concept is normally associated with failure to complete a construction contract. The application of liquidated and ascertained damages to maintenance contracts is far more difficult and requires clear criteria for a claim.

4.5.9 Withholding payment

A contract is a two-way agreement. Each party is promising to provide something to the other, and both have obligations. Withholding payment is not an automatic right of the purchaser of services and may even be a direct breach of the contract. Payment is becoming an important issue. 'Pay when paid' became illegal in 1998 and other attempts at delaying payment unfairly may also become subject to legal constraints. Payment may have to take place and reclaiming of money dealt with by taking legal action.

4.5.10 Letter of intent

A properly written letter of intent can have little value; it merely suggests that 'I may enter into a contract'. Whatever the value of such a letter, the intention of issuing it is to encourage a contractor to take the risk of preparing itself for that contract and perhaps to incur costs in the process. The issuer of the letter of intent may include a statement that it will pay any costs reasonably incurred by the contractor in making ready. This seems fair. Too often, the letter of intent is intended to obtain preparation but without liability for such costs. Any contractor prepared to incur costs under these arrangements is at risk and may well prefer to delay until something more formally binding is available.

4.5.11 Defects liability period

A properly completed construction project is expected to arrive at practical completion with a fully working system and a list of minor defects that can be corrected without disruption to the owner's enjoyment of the new facility. There is then a further 12 months (the defects liability period) in which the installation contractor must put these minor defects right and any others that may occur within the period. After that, the latent defects period is entered. Engineers generally have a tenuous grasp of this area.

During the defects liability period and beyond, the owner/occupier has a duty to maintain the installation. This starts from the day of handover, and includes the duty to operate the systems in accordance with the operation and maintenance instruction manual issued under the contract at handover, and in a way that will not harm the systems. If a client intends to use independent contractors to maintain an installation, the process of specification and tendering should have begun approximately six months before handover and to have been concluded before handover. This would enable contractors to be available for system demonstrations by the engineer and installation contractors.

Failure to provide adequate evidence of proper maintenance during the defects liability period will seriously undermine any attempt to mobilise construction warranties. The design engineer can become drawn in at this stage as terms such as 'maintenance free' are frequently used in life cycle costing reports associated with design selection decisions. The concept of maintenance is discussed in the CIBSE Technical Memoranda TM17[3], together with the role that inspection and actions such as lubrication play within it. 'Maintenance free' is not a recognised concept.

4.5.12 Consumable items and replacements

The definition of what is a consumable item and what is a replacement is important, particularly where the contract states the former is included within the contract while the latter is chargeable. The maintenance industry has a fairly clear understanding of the terms but they can be open to interpretation. *prEN 13306 Maintenance terminology*[10] defines a consumable item as 'maintenance material that is not item specific and not repairable'. Where the tenant/landlord relationship comes into the discussion, it becomes more important to define what is meant, and not to rely on common sense.

4.5.13 Permits-to-work

Many contracts refer to 'permit-to-work' systems but fail to recognise whether the contractor is in a position to issue such permits. Permits-to-work are a much misunderstood and misapplied concept.

In the field of high voltage electrical work, permits-to-work have a very specific meaning and relate to a codified process designed to save accidents and lives. Otherwise, any reference to them needs to consider the purpose of having such a system and address who is 'competent' to issue the permit. Competent in this instance should mean a person who has received sufficient instruction or training to have the judgement to fulfil the purpose of restricting and controlling access. The term has to apply to an individual and not a company.

The purpose of the permit may be to:

— prevent unexpected loss of service through unauthorised entry into a plant room or service route

— prevent injury to people entering plant areas

— identify the perpetrators of damage to plant or the dumping of rubbish.

Entry to plant rooms will need to be managed by a person who is present at all times that access to the plant rooms is possible. A maintenance technician who visits a site once per month is not able to do this. If damage or rubbish is the concern, any persons authorised to enter the room should be accompanied or the room revisited in their company before they leave site.

Plant rooms can be dangerous places. They should be kept locked and only people instructed in safe conduct in plant rooms should enter them unless accompanied by someone who is trained. Use as a storeroom should be prohibited.

4.6 Contract management

A key to the success of a contract is understanding that it will not happen unless it is managed. This will require some form of monitoring to ensure that the details of the specification are being followed. Section 6.7 in CIBSE Technical Memoranda TM17[3] describes this further and sets out typical elements to be included in a monitoring programme, plus guidance on how it should be carried out.

Quality assurance should also be adopted to ensure that documented procedures are in place and being followed. This will introduce the necessary controls, attitude and discipline to provide a consistent service to meet the client's expectations and requirements. The quality system being followed will need to incorporate flexibility to meet individual needs and to accommodate change during the contract period.

Recording of performance feedback, both technical and financial, can provide a valuable management tool. Technical feedback should aim to identify not only that maintenance is being correctly carried out, but also where it results in over- or undermaintenance, thus indicating that frequencies or specifications need to be modified. It is important to create an open environment for discussion with the contractor to allow the maintainer to put forward constructive comment.

Financial feedback will be primarily concerned with meeting budget expenditure plans. It should not be a simplistic comparison of overall expenditure against budget: there should be a detailed understanding of how individual areas have committed expenditure and, thus, where improvements and savings could be made in future.

Technical feedback should provide the impetus to make changes to the original strategy in the light of experience. Sufficient flexibility should exist for this, together with a formal procedure to record changes and their reasons.

Should the maintenance strategy not achieve the desired results, some means of enforcement may need to be adopted. Suggested options are improved supervision, better workforce motivation or some form of incentive. An example of this is defining objectives, monitoring results against targets and offering financial rewards if agreed targets are reached or exceeded. Financial incentives alone are recognised as not being a motivating force; attempts at motivation are more likely to be successful if regular opportunities are provided to discuss performance with supervisors and managers, to give encouragement, direction and support, and to generate enthusiasm about the work.

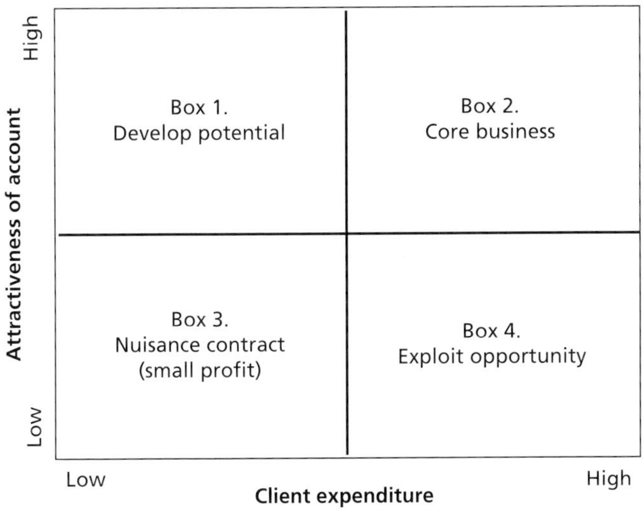

Figure 4.2 A simple contractor market matrix

It can be beneficial to assess the perceived position of the contractor within a market matrix in terms of the attractiveness of the client's account and the client's expenditure (see Figure 4.2). If the client makes this assessment and determines that it is in box 1 (Develop potential) in terms of the attractiveness of the account to the contractor and expenditure, it may find the contractor focusing on ways of generating income other than providing the expected service, possibly causing poor performance. In box 2 (Core business), the client can expect to be important to the contractor and receive the attention and performance specified. In box 3 (Nuisance), the contract may be viewed as a routine acquisition with little profit margin and the service could reflect this. In box 4 (Exploit opportunity) the contractor sees an opportunity for high income with a client that it may not wish to retain. From such an assessment, the client can be in a position to develop the relationship to where they wish to be positioned, for example in box 2.

References

1 *Joint Contracts Tribunal: JCT80 Standard form of building contract* (London: Royal Institute of British Architects) (1980)

2 *General conditions of contract for maintenance* Department of Environment QC/Works Form **C910** (London: The Stationery Office)

3 *Building services maintenance management* CIBSE Technical Memoranda **TM17** (London: Chartered Institution of Building Services Engineers) (1994)

4 Smith M *Maintenance contracts for building services* BSRIA Applications Guide **AG4/89.2** (Bracknell: Building Services Research and Information Association) (1992)

5 *Unfair Contract Terms Act 1977* (London: The Stationery Office) (1977)

6 *Supply of Goods and Services Act 1982* (London: The Stationery Office) (1982)

7 *Sale of Goods Act 1979* (London: The Stationery Office) (1979)

8 *Standard maintenance specification for mechanical services in buildings: Volume 1: Heating and pipework systems* HVCA **SMG90** (1990); *Volume 2: Ventilating and air conditioning* HVCA **SMG90b** (1991); *Volume 3: Control, energy and building management systems* HVCA **SMG90c** (1992); *Volume 4: Ancillaries, plumbing and sewerage* HVCA **SMG90d** (1992); *Volume 5: Electrics in buildings* HVCA **SMG90e** (London: Heating and Ventilating Contractors Association) (dates as indicated)

9 *Housing Grants, Construction and Regeneration Act 1966* (London: The Stationery Office) (1966)

10 *prEN:13306 Maintenance terminology* (London: British Standards Institution) (1998)

Bibliography

Rooley R Maintenance and refurbishment *Building Services Environmental Engineer* **21**(4) 11–18 (1997)

Model form of general conditions of contract, commentary: a practical guide (London: Association of Consulting Engineers) (1992)

Curtis B et al *Roles, responsibilities and risks in management contracting* CIRIA Special Publication 81 (London: Construction Industry Research and Information Association) (1991)

Chappell D, Powell-Smith V *JCT intermediate form of contract — a practical guide* (Epsom: Institute of Building Control) (1991)

Code of practice for project management for construction and development (Ascot: Chartered Institute of Building) (1996)

5 Maintenance strategy and control

Contents

Summary

Strategic considerations for maintenance are presented under two subheadings: design stage and operational stage.

A broad spectrum of factors affecting maintenance decisions is set out in the form of a checklist under each heading.

Maintenance monitoring and control techniques are outlined briefly with references to sources of comprehensive guidance. An introduction to operating oversized plant is also provided.

Buildings and their associated engineering services play a significant role in the achievement of corporate objectives of an organisation. Building services installations are largely responsible for the working environment of an establishment, and their operation and maintenance therefore form a crucial part of the total facilities management process.

The formulation of a maintenance strategy starts at the initial design stage of a building or a facility, with a critical appraisal of the maintenance implications of different design options carried out at the conceptual stage. The operation and maintenance strategy for the building and its engineering services should receive serious consideration by both building owners and occupiers. For owners, a building constructed to optimise maintenance and to match user requirements should be easy to rent or to sell. For occupiers, the effects of maintenance on core business objectives should be considered before buying, leasing or constructing a building.

At boardroom level, maintenance strategy is directed to improving the organisation's profitability, both in the short and long term. Inadequate or inappropriate maintenance will inevitably result in breakdowns. In the long term it could cause assets to depreciate more rapidly and, as a result, affect the company's prosperity. Over-maintaining will drain resources unnecessarily and could introduce problems such as maintenance-induced failures. Senior management responsible for the facility must establish the correct level of operation and maintenance and allocate adequate funds to carry out this work.

At the operational level, maintenance strategy is about improving production economies and the effectiveness of the maintenance organisation. This may require a culture change from using traditional approaches such as time-based activities to maintenance that is linked to the essential plant operating conditions. Planned preventive maintenance systems that require maintenance tasks to be performed at fixed frequencies irrespective of the plant condition could result in work that is not necessary or even maintenance-induced failures.

New technologies such as condition-based maintenance and diagnosis by expert systems enable the building services industry to determine the maintenance requirements of plant and equipment to suit the operational needs of the business more accurately than previously. This enables the maintenance activities to be carried out only when required to satisfy a business operational need. It is also important to note that any maintenance regime should not adopt a single approach to maintenance, i.e. reactive, preventive or predictive. It will be a combination of all such methods and their correct mix is essential for the optimisation of the maintenance regime (see section 3).

Quality management systems can be used by organisations to ensure maintenance is consistent and matches the business needs.

5.1 Maintenance strategy

The maintenance strategy for building services needs to be addressed at two stages of the life of plant and installations:

(*a*) the design stage

(*b*) the operational stage.

5.1.1 Design stage

The starting point for the maintenance strategy is the design (see section 2). Designers must evaluate maintenance requirements of different design options. They should also consider the extent to which maintenance can be designed out and how support systems can be built into the installation to facilitate efficient and cost-effective operation and maintenance.

Some key issues that need consideration are:

(*a*) Positioning and sizing of plant rooms and access to plant:

— human, vehicular and materials traffic

- access for operation, maintenance and refurbishment
- storage

(*b*) Plant reliability, availability and the provision of redundant systems:

- user requirement for plant availability
- reliability of the systems, plant and components
- likely down-time (repair time as well as the time required to carry out diagnosis and to obtain spares and, where necessary, specialist labour)

(*c*) Requirement for specialist knowledge for maintenance and its availability:

- specialist versus non-specialist plant
- local availability of specialists and cost
- training requirements

(*d*) Requirement for specialist labour for maintenance and its availability:

- specialist versus non-specialist plant
- local availability of specialist labour and cost
- local availability of specialist tools and cost
- training requirements

(*e*) Spares requirement and availability:

- local availability of spare parts
- delivery periods
- cost of spares

(*f*) After-sales support from the suppliers of plant and systems:

- technical support
- proximity of the company, agents or representatives
- financial standing of the supplier

(*g*) Standardisation of plant and components:

- to reduce down-time
- to minimise stock level of spares

(*h*) Built-in systems for monitoring and feedback of plant status:

- building management systems
- condition monitoring equipment

(*i*) Designing out maintenance:

- components requiring no maintenance
- increased mean time between failure

(*j*) Ease of maintenance:

- accessibility
- simplicity
- established versus new technology.

(*k*) Health and safety considerations — see sections 17 and 18.

Throughout the design process, the designer should liaise closely with the building owner or occupier and the facility or maintenance manager to establish the maintenance implications of the design proposals. The designer should identify the best design solution to match organisational needs giving consideration to operation and maintenance and whole-life strategies as well as other performance issues (e.g. safety, energy and change to environment). When selecting a particular design solution, the options may be limited by client restrictions on capital availability, although it may be possible to justify a preferred option by reduced overall life cycle costs.

It is not normally possible to reduce the factors described above to a common denominator such as a monetary equivalent. The decision as to the best design solution to fit maintenance and other organisational needs is often a subjective judgement based on a comparison between qualitative and quantitative aspects.

5.1.2 Building operational stage

As described previously, the performance of building services is important to the operations of an organisation. Senior management has the responsibility for setting the policy for wider issues of operation and maintenance of building services that will affect the organisation's corporate objectives. This involves deciding:

- the level of risk the organisation is willing to tolerate: e.g. financial, business loss, health and safety, employee satisfaction
- method of resourcing maintenance: e.g. in-house, outsource, mixed
- budgets: e.g. level of finance available for maintenance, financial targets
- bench marks: cost targets, performance targets.

At this stage, maintenance strategy should be to establish the level of operation and maintenance that needs to be carried out to match the expectations of the organisation. Key criteria that need consideration are:

- compliance with the requirements of legislation and authoritative bodies
- improving the health and safety of the building users and those who operate and maintain the plant
- functions of plant and equipment that are critical to company objectives
- optimising plant reliability and availability to sustain those critical to company objectives
- optimising the utilisation of resources
- satisfying other key objectives of the organisation
- safeguarding assets.

Once the level of operation and maintenance required to satisfy the company objectives is understood, it is the responsibility of the operational management to:

- carry out risk assessments
- establish the health and safety policy (e.g. level of action to achieve the company objectives for health

and safety, allocation of responsibilities and establishing action plans)

- establish the operation and maintenance policy (e.g. level of planned versus corrective maintenance, run to failure and condition monitoring)
- develop information systems for operation and maintenance (e.g. method of record keeping such as computer-based, manual, location or archiving; nature of records to be kept such as asset registers or planned maintenance log books; and responsibilities for maintaining records)
- procure and manage operation and maintenance activities (e.g. in-house; out-sourcing such as term contracts, lump-sum contracts or facilities management contracts; mix between in-house and external resources)
- set performance targets to meet the bench marks determined by senior management (e.g. cost, plant availability, response times, quality of records, quality of workmanship)
- set budgets (allocating finance to each function)
- monitor performance
- provide feedback to senior management
- organise improvements or changes to suit evolving business needs.

Detailed information on these subjects can be found in various textbooks on maintenance management, CIBSE Technical Memoranda TM17 *Building services maintenance management*[1] and BSRIA publications[2–8].

5.2 Control of maintenance

Controlling operation and maintenance is an ongoing activity. It is the process of continually monitoring the maintenance system and its performance against pre-set goals, and reporting the performance to the management responsible for these functions. Where performances fail to achieve set targets, changes to the maintenance regime should be made to correct any deviations. Alternatively, where failure is consistent, the targets themselves may be unrealistic or unattainable and may need to be reviewed and changed.

A quality management system for the maintenance function will define roles and responsibilities and establish procedures and reporting formats, thereby helping to ensure consistent and effective control.

Controlling maintenance usually requires two levels of audit:

(*a*) A system audit to check the detailed formal procedures that constitute the maintenance regime (e.g. procedures for planned maintenance, procedures for record keeping and managerial procedures) to ensure that they satisfy legal requirements and company objectives.

(*b*) A performance audit to monitor the performance of the maintenance regime against set bench marks (e.g. cost targets, response times, plant down-time and quality of records).

5.3 Operating oversized plant

Many existing systems contain oversized plant, which can result in excessive energy consumption, instabilities at low loads, an undermining of the economic life of the plant, premature equipment failure etc. It is estimated that oversizing is typically responsible for approximately 10–15% of energy consumption for heating, ventilation and air conditioning. Plant oversizing is rarely a deliberate decision, but more often the cumulative result of a number of factors including:

- in-built allowances in design data and calculation procedures
- margins added during the design process
- specified client requirements being in excess of operational needs
- changes that occur after the design stages, e.g. to fabric and glazing specifications
- difficulties in matching system requirements to available equipment: proprietary equipment ranges often come in standard sizes with large increments between product capacities.

The cumulative impact of these is that most systems contain some degree of oversizing; indeed it is estimated that fans and pumps are usually oversized by at least 10–15% while boiler and chiller plants can be oversized by anything up to a factor of 2.

In view of this it is very much in the interests of the occupier not to allow the operation of oversized plant to continue. To meet this aim, the occupier should look to the facilities manager, first, to identify what plant is oversized and, secondly, to advise on what to do to improve matters.

Pointers that could indicate oversizing include:

(*a*) design conditions easily maintained even in extreme weather

(*b*) relatively short warm-up/cool-down times

(*c*) plant modules that never operate or plant (e.g. boilers and water chillers) that never runs continuously, even in extreme weather

(*d*) drive motor running currents well below the full-load current

(*e*) distribution system temperature differentials that never reach the declared design parameters

(*f*) control valves serving heating/cooling coils never fully open (under steady state conditions) and tending to 'hunt'

(*g*) CO_2 levels in accommodation always below 600 ppm (indicative of excess ventilation).

Performance monitoring over a reasonable period and extending over all weather conditions, including the appropriate seasonal extremes, is necessary to confirm oversizing. The monitoring also needs to include some attempt to indicate the degree of oversizing. To assist in finalising the assessment, consideration should be given to using a commissioning specialist to check performances under varying conditions and to help tie down the causes and effects.

Where oversizing has been identified, action needs to be taken to reduce energy consumption and improve plant efficiency. Prospective actions can vary considerably in cost (and, hence, payback prospects) and may include:

(*a*) isolate, drain down and 'mothball' plant modules surplus to requirements

(*b*) reduce the driven speed of belt-driven equipment to match measured requirements

(*c*) reduce fluid volume flow rates in distribution systems to match measured requirements

(*d*) use reduced size components in control valves or dampers to give better control (but avoid abrupt pipe/duct contractions)

(*e*) isolate terminal units, emitters and air distribution outlets (or inlets)

(*f*) reduce fresh air volume flow rates to match requirements more closely

(*g*) check the control regime generally and ensure that plant operating times are trimmed to an absolute minimum.

When taking corrective actions on plant operation it is unreasonable to expect adjustments to be right the first time. There should be a readiness to try several increments of adjustment, progressively homing in on the optimum setting.

References

1 *Building services maintenance management* CIBSE Technical Memoranda **TM17** (London: Chartered Institution of Building Services Engineers) (1994)

2 Parsloe C *Design for maintainability* BSRIA Application Guide **AG11/92** (Bracknell: Building Services Research and Information Association) (1992)

3 Armstrong J *Condition monitoring — an introduction to its application in building services* BSRIA Technical Note **TN1/86** (Bracknell: Building Services Research and Information Association) (1986)

4 *Condition based maintenance for building services* BSRIA Technical Note **TN1/95** (Bracknell: Building Services Research and Information Association) (1995)

5 *Infrared condition based maintenance for building services* BSRIA Technical Note **TN2/95** (Bracknell: Building Services Research and Information Association) (1995)

6 Barnard N and Starr A *Condition monitoring for building services* BSRIA Technical Note **TN3/95** (Bracknell: Building Services Research and Information Association) (1995)

7 Barnard N and Starr A *BEMS as condition based maintenance tools* BSRIA Technical Note **TN4/95** (Bracknell: Building Services Research and Information Association) (1995)

8 Nanayakkara R and Smith M H *Operation and maintenance audits* BSRIA Application Guide **AG24/97** (Bracknell: Building Services Research and Information Association) (1997)

Bibliography

Brittain J R *Oversized air handling plant* BSRIA Guidance Note **GN11/97** (Bracknell: Building Services Research and Information Association) (1997)

Brittain J R *Oversized heating plant* BSRIA Guidance Note **GN12/97** (Bracknell: Building Services Research and Information Association) (1997)

Brittain J R *Oversized cooling and pumping plant* BSRIA Guidance note **GN13/97** (Bracknell: Building Services Research and Information Association) (1997)

6 Energy efficiency and maintenance

Contents

Summary

Techniques by which the maintenance team might improve energy efficiency are outlined, starting with good housekeeping. In addition to input from the maintenance team, this requires support from building occupants and commitment from management.

The importance of maintenance staff 'knowing' their building and being aware of hot (and cold) spots is noted; the importance of the automatic controls system is stressed.

With ventilation and air conditioning, simple things such as regularly changing or cleaning filters can help to reduce fan power; with refrigerating systems trained personnel can ensure that the systems operate to optimum efficiency.

Hints for improving the effectiveness of artificial lighting are provided, routine boiler efficiency checks for heating and hot water services systems are recommended and it is suggested that the merits of variable volume pumping be considered for some water distribution systems.

Finally, it is pointed out that the maintenance engineer or contractor should prepare supporting financial justification for any energy efficiency improvement proposals.

With the continuing escalation of international competition, business efficiency and cost management in all its forms becomes increasingly important. All businesses use energy in some way in their operational regime and energy efficiency can offer a ready means of making cost reductions. For any drive towards improved energy efficiency to succeed, however, there must be unreserved commitment from the building user's top management.

In the UK, the cost of energy is such that fuel and utility costs tend to be small in comparison with premises rental and wages bills; nevertheless the potential for savings can be significant and should not be overlooked.

Awareness of energy efficiency was well developed in the 1970s but the effort to conserve energy resources appears to have relaxed significantly since then. The justifiable worldwide environmental concerns regarding global warming and the associated need to reduce CO_2 emissions seem set to revitalise the attitude to energy efficiency, albeit from a different viewpoint to the conservation of world energy resources.

Any business seeking to improve its operational energy efficiency would probably initially look for in-house leadership from its facilities manager. The facilities manager would, in turn, probably consult the maintenance specialist to tap its overall knowledge of the building services.

To meet such a request for advice and guidance, maintenance engineers need to move beyond keeping the plant in good working order, although this is important in itself. As a minimum, they should be able to comment on the scope for varying the operational modes of systems to match the actual usage of the building more closely. This may include proposing the cost effective use of variable speed drives for fans and pumps to match heating or air conditioning system performance diversity and seasonal variations. The same principles may be applied to process services such as kitchen ventilation where system performance could be matched to the operational demand. The actual technique employed for drive speed variation may be multi-speed motors or inverter speed control.

The fundamental commitment to energy efficiency must derive from, and receive the full support of, the building user's senior management.

The remainder of this section details a series of techniques that may be appropriate to enhance energy efficiency in particular applications.

6.1 Energy efficiency options

6.1.1 Good housekeeping

The maintenance department plays an important part in energy efficiency, but the concept must extend to all occupants of the building.

The overall approach and the level of diligence applied will depend on the energy policy of the particular business venture. Whichever level of application is involved, line management throughout the organisation should have specific responsibilities with respect to energy efficiency. Where appropriate, this may be developed to encourage some form of interdepartmental competitiveness provided that this does not deflect from business objectives.

In the same way that companies have used quality circles to focus the corporate attitude to quality, energy circles could be set up to improve performance in this respect. Another means of widening interest is staff suggestion schemes, which may be arranged to reward energy efficiency proposals in the same way as those for business efficiency.

To ensure that occupants understand fully the most effective way to operate the building services systems and to maximise the benefit from passive provisions (e.g. sunblinds), a user's handbook should be provided. The building occupier may find that the original design team for the services installations is best placed to produce such a manual.

Other very simple but effective measures which derive from general occupant awareness are closing windows and doors and switching off lights and electrical appliances when not required.

One of the most effective measures for energy efficiency, and probably the simplest to apply, is to monitor space temperatures to ensure that overheating or overcooling do not occur. While a building management system (BMS) would provide the easiest means of monitoring, it is advisable to carry out an occasional tour of the building to compare measured temperatures with those recorded. In this connection, it should be noted that the *Fuel and Electricity (Heating) (Control) Order 1974*(1) and its subsequent amendment(2) remain as statutes and require that fuel and electricity shall not be used to maintain temperatures above 19 °C.

A further refinement of simple temperature monitoring is a regime of energy monitoring and targeting. This entails checking and recording energy usage in all its forms, identifying profligate areas and setting future targets for on-going improvements. Where the energy bills are large, it may be worth installing sub-metering to aid the identification of energy 'black spots'. The facilities manager may seek energy-use comparisons with other buildings of a similar nature; the series of Energy Efficiency Best Practice documents produced by the Building Research Energy Conservation Support Unit (available from the Building Research Establishment, Garston, Watford WD2 7JR) are very useful in this respect.

Where out-of-hours or overtime working is required, the facilities manager should assess means of economically maintaining space temperatures for the occupants involved. Only as a last resort should the central air conditioning or heating systems be operated.

6.1.2 Building fabric

All buildings have cold spots (or hot spots). Very often these areas are the top floors of buildings (due to roof exposure) or corner rooms (with two exposed wall faces). Facilities and premises managers should make it their business to know where these areas are and, where possible, use their influence to restrict usage to applications less sensitive to temperature control. Ideally, they should also seek cost effective measures to improve the situation.

Building interior decor can have a significant influence on illuminance levels. Light coloured walls and, particularly, ceilings can improve the lighting level on horizontal work surfaces. The use of light coloured work surfaces, however, can be counter effective in this respect due to 'glare' or reflected light interfering with occupants' vision.

6.1.3 Control systems

See also section 8.

Control systems can be complex. As well as trying to ensure that a control system is performing its function effectively, premises managers also need to ask whether the system in question is manageable. Do they understand the system fully? Can they manage the maintenance of the system efficiently and economically? If the answer to such questions is 'no', the need for a change is indicated. Perhaps the control system should be simplified or, possibly, the premises manager and maintenance team be given better training. The solution will depend on the particular situation.

Calibration of control sensors is a critical factor in ensuring that a control system functions properly. In some instances, recalibration of controls is a demanding requirement consuming a significant proportion of the system maintenance costs. The replacement of sensors with better quality components can reduce, or even eliminate, the problem of set-point drift as well as improving energy efficiency.

Once again, simple disciplines can exert a strong, positive influence on energy efficiency. Checks on time switches and optimiser controls to ensure that the settings are as intended — and that these settings are appropriate to the operational regime of the business — are an important maintenance routine.

Where occupants are provided with control interfaces, it is important that they appreciate the mode of operation that will give the best results. Again, this information should be given in a user's handbook.

For centralised system controls, access should be restricted to authorised personnel with the appropriate training and expertise. Even these operatives should be instructed to modify control settings only in accordance with proposals that have been properly discussed and agreed. Unauthorised tampering with controls must be avoided.

In summary, the operation and maintenance team must be fully in control of the controls system.

6.1.4 Refrigeration systems

It is important that the operation and maintenance of refrigeration systems is carried out only by trained personnel with the appropriate expertise. The Refrigerant Handling Certification Scheme operated by the Air Conditioning and Refrigeration Industry Board provides some scope for evaluating competence in this respect. Skill and expertise are essential for effective monitoring of the factors that influence the efficient operation of a refrigeration system, including refrigerant charge levels;

compressor cycling; and pressures and temperatures throughout the refrigeration system circuits.

Water treatment needs to be applied and maintained to keep heat exchange surfaces clean and to maximise efficiency. This applies particularly to units with evaporative cooling where water treatment is crucial to the control of algae and microbial and bacterial activity, including legionellosis.

Refrigerating efficiency can be improved significantly by allowing the condensing pressure to vary on a seasonal basis. Where this facility is not included in the installation, advice should be sought from the manufacturer.

6.1.5 Lighting

Starting with the simplest and most economic options, every effort should be made to ensure the best use of daylight. This may require action to minimise solar gain and to ensure glare does not cause a nuisance to occupants.

Automatic dimming control of luminaires near to windows can be used as part of the daylight regime. Provision for lighting switching should be arranged to match the usage of the accommodation. For cellular layouts this would entail individual switching while in open plan areas switching arrangements should ideally coincide with departmental 'boundaries'. Where the switching match is poor, wiring circuit provisions should be investigated to see if there is scope for improvement.

Maintenance routines can improve lighting efficiency by using a regular programme of cleaning for lighting diffusers and by replacing luminaires as they become less efficient with age.

There may also be advantages in replacing older type tubular fluorescent lamps with modern, improved efficiency units with an equivalent lighting output.

6.1.6 Heating and hot water services systems

Periodic boiler efficiency tests, checks on boiler cycling, ensuring that system air venting is good, distribution temperature checks to highlight insulation deficiencies and monitoring of control set-points all have a contribution to make to energy efficiency.

The calibration of the set-points for frost and condensation protection should be checked routinely to ensure that actuation temperatures are kept as low as practicable. As most buildings have a high thermal capacity and take a long time to cool, the actuation setting for condensation protection systems should be experimentally reduced so that the true need is established.

Temperatures of hot water systems need to be kept at appropriate levels to minimise legionellosis risk but there is usually some scope for timing the operating hours.

Variable speed pumping should be considered wherever the heating load profile shows this to be worthwhile.

6.1.7 Electric motors

At the simplest level, ensure as far as possible that the rating of electric motors is appropriate to the required duty. The use of variable speed drives wherever feasible and cost effective has already been referred to in this section. To put this recommendation into perspective, a fan or pump drive motor operating at half speed reduces power consumption by more than 85%.

6.2 Justification of proposals

In preparing proposals for energy efficiency improvements, whether on their own initiative or at the request of management, premises managers should determine the costs of implementation and assess, as accurately as possible, the potential savings likely to result. Section 13 provides guidance on the presentation of these cost data to demonstrate the viability of the proposals, while section 14 provides information on the economic life of equipment and components which may comprise part of the proposal.

6.3 Further guidance

Particular sources of further guidance on energy efficiency include the CIBSE (in particular, CIBSE Guide F: *Energy efficiency in buildings*[3]), the Department of the Environment, Transport and Regions, the Energy Technology Support Unit and the Building Research Energy Conservation Support Unit.

References

1 *The Fuel and Electricity (Heating) (Control) Order 1974* Statutory Instrument 1974 No. 2160 (London: The Stationery Office) (1974)

2 *The Fuel and Electricity (Heating) (Control) (Amendment) Order 1980* Statutory Instrument 1980 No. 1013 (London: The Stationery Office) (1980)

3 *Energy efficiency in buildings* CIBSE Guide F (London: Chartered Institution of Building Services Engineers) (1998)

Bibliography

Armstrong J *The effect of maintenance on boiler efficiency* BSRIA Technical Note **TN5/83** (Bracknell: Building Services Research and Information Association) (1983)

Building services maintenance management CIBSE Technical Memoranda **TM17** (London: Chartered Institution of Building Services Engineers) (1994)

CIBSE Code for interior lighting (London: Chartered Institution of Building Services Engineers) (1994)

Commercial refrigeration plant: energy efficient operation and maintenance DETR **GPG36** (London: Department of Environment Transport and Regions) (1992)

Energy efficient lighting in buildings Thermie Maxibrochure (Garston: Building Research Energy Conservation Support Unit/OPET) (1993)

Fault-finding procedures in the building services industry BSRIA Technical Note **TN12/86** (Bracknell: Building Services Research and Information Association) (1986)

Industrial refrigeration plant: energy efficient operation and maintenance DETR **GPG42** (London: Department of Environment Transport and Regions) (1992)

Introduction to energy efficiency in buildings Energy Efficiency Booklets 1–13 (London: Department of Environment, Transport and Regions) (1994)

Maintaining the efficient operation of heating and hot water. A guide for managers DETR **GPG188** (London: Department of Environment, Transport and Regions) (1996)

Smith M H *Maintenance and utility costs — results of a survey* BSRIA Technical Memoranda **TM3/91** (Bracknell: Building Services Research and Information Association) (1991)

Standard maintenance specification for mechanical services in buildings: Volume 1: Heating and pipework systems HVCA **SMG90** (1990); *Volume 2: Ventilating and air conditioning* HVCA **SMG90b** (1991); *Volume 3: Control, energy and building management systems* HVCA **SMG90c** (1992); *Volume 4: Ancillaries, plumbing and sewerage* HVCA **SMG90d** (1992); *Volume 5: Electrics in buildings* HVCA **SMG90e** (London: Heating and Ventilating Contractors Association) (dates as indicated)

7 Plant service frequencies

Contents

Summary

The part played by regular maintenance in promoting efficient plant operation and prolonging plant life is recognised and the statutory requirement for servicing to particular plant items is highlighted.

The relevance of manufacturers' maintenance instructions in relation to warranties is noted and the typical frequencies and standard frequencies as set-out in industry specifications are referred to.

The direct relationship of maintenance frequencies to the labour element of a contract is noted and the adjustment of service frequencies to suit particular applications is recommended.

An appendix outlines statutory requirements for inspection under PUWER and LOLER

The purpose of regular servicing is to sustain the operating efficiency of plant and to prolong its economic life.

Servicing will incur labour costs and require the provision of materials such as consumables (e.g. lubricants) or replacement components. The life-cycle cost for serviced plant will therefore comprise its initial capital cost, any replacement costs and its service costs over its complete life. There will be an optimum situation where these cost components combine to offer a minimum life-cycle cost for the plant.

The establishment of an optimum service frequency for plant or equipment would require a great deal of trial and error or an extensive database. While optimum frequencies would be ideal, they would be dependent on too many factors to represent a realistic goal. Service frequencies applied in practice may be derived from a variety of sources including:

(*a*) statutory requirements (for instance, as required by health and safety or other legislation)

(*b*) manufacturers' recommendations

(*c*) typical frequencies

(*d*) 'standard' frequencies.

7.1 Statutory service frequencies

The service frequencies for a number of items where soundness of the plant has a strong bearing on health and safety (e.g. some pressure vessels and lifting gear) form part of the requirements of the statutory health and safety legislation (see appendix 7.A1). Maximum service intervals are quoted for such equipment and, in some instances, these may appear to be unusual frequencies. This is because they are based on typical frequencies with an additional period allowed for the administration of logistics (e.g. 1 year + 2 months = 14 months). Any extension beyond the maximum service intervals becomes a breach of statute and could expose the building operator to action from the Health and Safety Executive.

7.2 Manufacturer recommendations

Manufacturers of plant and equipment usually publish maintenance guidance or instructions for issue with their products. This documentation comprises details of the service or maintenance attention required together with a recommended frequency of attention.

In general, manufacturers' maintenance recommendations are standard lists compiled with no knowledge of the particular application of the product. For this reason, these instructions tend to err on the safe side and the maintenance frequencies quoted are often generous. In applying manufacturers' recommendations, it is prudent to review maintenance frequencies continually to achieve an optimum or more cost-effective regime (see section 7.6).

Where it is apparent that a manufacturer's maintenance instructions have not been followed, this may be claimed to invalidate equipment warranties or guarantees. In the event of a premature failure of a product, therefore, evidence of compliance with the manufacturer's instructions may be an important consideration.

7.3 Typical service frequencies

Typical maintenance frequencies are, for convenience, based on calendar increments (e.g. daily, weekly, fortnightly, monthly, quarterly, six-monthly, annually and multiples of years). In some instances, the selection of a frequency for a particular maintenance function is fairly arbitrary while, for other applications, extensive statistical data may be available. The important consideration is that a frequency must be appropriate to the specific application and take account of all relevant conditions of the usage.

With plant where the operational duty is predominantly seasonal (e.g. heating boilers), major servicing requirements should be scheduled to ensure no interference with availability of the plant when it is most required.

7.4 'Standard' service frequencies

The most effective approach to what might be termed 'standard' maintenance frequencies are those published by the Heating and Ventilating Contractors' Association (HVCA) in its comprehensive *Standard maintenance specifications for mechanical services in buildings* (1). These standards are produced jointly by the HVCA and CIBSE with wide collaboration from the building services industry. The maintenance frequencies may, therefore, be considered to reflect a broad spectrum of opinion and should be appropriate for a wide range of applications.

7.5 Inviting tenders

Maintenance costs derive from the service applied and its frequency; because of labour cost implications, the latter probably exerts the most significant long-term influence. To ensure equitability of tendering it is essential to state the required service frequencies in the tender documentation as well as details of the maintenance to be carried-out.

For tendering purposes, arbitrary service frequencies may be stated, with more appropriate service intervals being arrived at by negotiation with the successful tenderer based on its quoted schedule of rates. Alternatively, both the servicing and the frequencies may be stipulated as being in accordance with the HVCA/CIBSE *Standard maintenance specifications for mechanical services in buildings* (1).

7.6 Adjustment of service frequencies

While it is acknowledged that the goal of establishing ideal, optimum service frequencies may be unrealistic, this argument should not be extended to the general acceptance of service frequencies. These should be continually reviewed and, where appropriate, challenged.

For example, a possible indication of a need for more frequent servicing (or a different mode of service) could be the frequent failure of a particular component or mechanism. Conversely, where there is no loss of performance efficiency of a particular mechanism, there may be scope for an increase in the intervals between servicing.

Generally, marginal increases in service frequencies can be made with reasonable confidence and, with a large-scale operation, can result in worthwhile savings on labour. For there to be confidence in significant extensions of service intervals there would need to be supporting considerations. These may take the form of condition monitoring or wide-ranging, long-term records of maintenance experience with similar plant and equipment. It may also be advisable to discuss any proposed extensions of maintenance intervals with the equipment manufacturer.

To promote the principle of reducing unnecessary maintenance, team incentive schemes have been devised which reward reduced maintenance attention but penalise plant breakdowns. While such schemes are more likely to be applied to production machinery, the concept could be used for building engineering services maintenance.

References

1 *Standard maintenance specification for mechanical services in buildings: Volume 1: Heating and pipework systems* HVCA **SMG90** (1990); *Volume 2: Ventilating and air conditioning* HVCA **SMG90b** (1991); *Volume 3: Control, energy and building management systems* HVCA **SMG90c** (1992); *Volume 4: Ancillaries, plumbing and sewerage* HVCA **SMG90d** (1992); *Volume 5: Electrics in buildings* HVCA **SMG90e** (London: Heating and Ventilating Contractors Association) (dates as indicated)

Appendix 7.A1: Statutory regulations affecting plant service requirements

The Provision and Use of Work Equipment Regulations 1998[1] PUWER 98) relates to the provision of work equipment and its safe use. The regulations require consideration to be given to:

- the nature and degree of risk associated with the equipment and its use
- the means available to reduce those risks.

The Lifting Operations and Lifting Equipment Regulations 1998[2] (LOLER) applies in addition to the requirements of PUWER 98, for lifting equipment and lifting operations. These regulations require:

- the planning, supervision and execution of lifting operations to ensure safety
- the safe use of lifting equipment
- the periodic thorough examination of lifting equipment by a competent person.

These regulations became effective in 1998. They place strict requirements on all employers to consider the hazards connected with the use of work and lifting equipment and reduce the associated risks.

PUWER 98 requires that, where the risk assessment carried out under the requirements of *The Management of Health and Safety at Work Regulations 1992*[3] has identified a significant risk to the operator or other workers from the installation or the use of the work equipment, a suitable inspection should be carried out. Inspections should be undertaken by persons who have the necessary knowledge and experience to do so.

Where the work equipment is of a type where the safe operation is critically dependent on its condition in use and deterioration would lead to a significant risk to the operator or other person, the frequency of the inspections should be based on how quickly the work equipment is likely to deteriorate and therefore give rise to significant risk.

The scope of equipment requiring inspection, the type of person considered most appropriate for undertaking inspections and the recommended maximum periodicities are detailed in Table 1. Note that the tables are non-exclusive. They indicate where the inherent risks from the installation or use of the work equipment would normally be such to warrant inspection by an independent competent person (C), where inspection by an appropriately trained and qualified person would normally be adequate (T) and where normally only the result of a risk assessment would be able to determine which of the two inspection routes is appropriate (T/C).

The indicated inspection periods are for guidance only. The risks imposed by work equipment and its performance must be evaluated by the client or by an organisation competent to do so.

LOLER Regulation 9 requires the thorough examination of lifting equipment at specified situations. Unlike previous lifting legislation where the scope of lifting equipment requiring thorough examination was clearly defined, LOLER does not define what equipment needs to be thoroughly examined. LOLER gives the owner of

Table 1 Guidance list of work equipment requiring inspection

Item	Competent or trained person	Recommended maximum periodicity (months)
Doors — sliding	T	12
Automatic/revolving doors	T	12
Escalators (PM45)	C	6
Fire doors and fire curtains	C	12
Food processing equipment	T	12
Guards and safety equipment	C	6
Guillotine (moveable/fixed guard)	C	6
Ladders/steps/stairs	T	12
Masts, radio & TV	C	12
Racking/warehouse stillage	T/C	12
Safety harness (if not under LOLER)	C	12
Gymnast equipment (if not under LOLER)	C	12
Stage equipment (also LOLER)	C	12
Waste compactors	C	12
Waste disposal units	T	12

C indicates inspection by competent person; T indicates inspection by person trained and qualified to make such inspections of equipment concerned is sufficient under normal circumstances

Table 2 Guidance list of lifting equipment requiring examination

Item	Examination periodicity (months)
Passenger hoist/lift	6
Goods only hoist/lift	12
Passenger/goods hoist/lift	6
Service lift	12
Home lift	6
Paternoster passenger lift	6
Paternoster goods only lift	12
Scissor lift	6
Stair lift	6
Teagle lift	12
Patient lift	6
Winches/capstans	12
Blocks, ropes, hoist, pulleys etc	12
Bosunís chair	6
Harness with lanyard	6
Safety belts	6
Supports for lifting gantry equipment	12
Eyebolts	6
Cradle	6
Fork lift truck attachments	6
Lifting beams/frames	6
Shackles	6
Slings	6
Suspended access equipment	6
Window cleaning rig	6
Fork lift truck	6
Stage equipment hoist	6
Gymnasium equipment	12
Roller shutter doors	12

lifting equipment the option of adhering to a new set of prescribed periodicities for thorough examination or to have in place or to follow a scheme of examination produced by a competent person.

The types of lifting equipment requiring thorough examination by a competent person and the recommended periodicities for those examinations are detailed in Table 2.

References

1 *The Provision and Use of Work Equipment Regulations 1998* Statutory Instrument 1998 No. 2306 (London: The Stationery Office) (1998)

2 *The Lifting Operations and Lifting Equipment Regulations 1998* Statutory Instrument 1998 No. 2307 (London: The Stationery Office) (1998)

3 *The Health and Safety at Work Regulations 1992* Statutory Instrument 1992 No. 2051 (London: The Stationery Office) (1992)

Bibliography

Simple guide to The Provision and Use of Work Equipment Regulations 1998 HSE **INDG290** (London: Health and Safety Executive) (1999)

Simple guide to The Lifting Operations and Lifting Equipment Regulations 1998 HSE **INDG291** (London: Health and Safety Executive) (1999)

8 Heating, ventilating and air conditioning controls

Contents

Summary

In discussing the purpose of controls, reference is made to the importance of providing building occupants with the ability to regulate their own environment and ensuring that they understand how the control system operates. A user's handbook is recommended.

Regarding the maintenance of controls, the possible need for periodic recommissioning is highlighted and the maintenance benefits of better quality sensors and control equipment is outlined.

The advantages of monitoring contract performance are noted and examples given of contract options particular to controls maintenance.

Typical routine maintenance checks for controls are outlined, with particular reference to building management systems.

Finally, the scope for exploiting the continual development of controls technology to effect viable upgrading of control systems is discussed.

For most building services installations, the single most significant factor in deviations in system performance is the malfunction of automatic controls. Similarly, control irregularities are a significant cause of excessive energy consumption.

These malfunctions or irregularities may be the result of an inappropriate controls concept, poor design of the control system, poor equipment selection (e.g. low quality sensors, oversized control valves or dampers), incorrect commissioning or inadequate maintenance. Any one of these shortcomings is capable of producing serious adverse effects.

While maintenance may not be responsible for a particular fault in a control system, competent and dedicated maintenance attention has the scope to rectify problems originating from earlier work. This can even include improvements to the control system design. This places maintenance of controls in a powerful position to exert a favourable influence on the performance and operational efficiency of the building services installation.

8.1 Purpose of controls

The fundamental purpose of building engineering services controls, whether automatic or manual, is to regulate the performance of systems to meet operational environmental requirements, in accordance with the design intent. In most instances the designer takes account of energy efficiency in selecting control sequences and set-point parameters.

Surveys of building users have shown that occupants accept building services installations more readily where they are able to intervene in the control system to some degree and to exercise their own preferences. In its simplest form, this may entail opening a window to increase ventilation or adjusting a thermostatic radiator valve to influence space temperature. Similarly, it can be beneficial to offer occupants a measure of influence on automatic control set-points (e.g. a warmer/cooler control knob offering, say, a 2 K temperature range).

It is of paramount importance that the design intent is made clear to building users and occupants. For simple building service installations, such as low temperature hot water (LTHW) heating systems, this may be virtually self-evident. Other installations, such as air conditioning systems, may be quite complex with various operating modes and sophisticated control sequences. The 'good practice' approach is for the system designer to provide a full design description covering all building services systems and their control concepts. This should describe the way the systems are intended to operate and may be supported by schematic diagrams to clarify particular operational details. Control sequences to regulate the operation of the system and to specify design set-point parameters may be included within the design description or presented as a separate document.

The design description should be aimed primarily at the building user and compiled in everyday language. For the sake of clarity and comprehension, it is important to avoid jargon, to define engineering terms and to ensure that the complete document is relevant to the particular installation.

Particular care should be taken to describe fully the scope the building occupier has to adjust the operation of the systems to suit their specific requirements. In this respect, it may be helpful to schedule all system control parameter set-points and to indicate reasonable ranges of adjustment to facilitate resetting by authorised personnel where this is shown to be appropriate. Such a schedule should also include comments on the likely effect of set-point adjustments on operational energy efficiency as well as occupant comfort.

Ideally, the designer should provide a user's handbook to guide the building occupants on how to gain maximum benefit from the environmental systems. Again, this should be easy to understand with, where possible, illustrations to aid comprehension. Where a user's handbook is not provided as part of the installation contract, the building occupier should consider separately commissioning the designer to produce one.

8.2 Maintenance requirements

Given that controls have such a significant influence on system performance and energy efficient operation, their maintenance requires careful attention. But what is the maintenance requirement? An industry standard approach to such needs is provided by the Heating and Ventilating Contractors Association's *Standard maintenance specification for mechanical services in buildings*[1].

Mechanical maintenance of manual controls and automatic control actuators is obviously necessary to ensure that these operate smoothly over their complete range. This is not enough, however. There is also a requirement for the maintenance engineer to check the set-points and calibration of all control sensors, but even this is not sufficient to ensure satisfactory operation of the control system. The maintenance engineer should monitor the performance of the system, have an awareness of the reactions of occupants to the environment the system provides and, in effect, constantly challenge the effectiveness of the controls system and its concept.

The result of this approach is, in effect, a continuous fine-tuning of the controls system. For this to be fully effective the maintenance engineer must keep a careful, written record of all changes and adjustments and annotate the plant logbooks or database accordingly.

This requires a high standard of expertise and commitment from the controls maintenance specialist. In terms of expertise, in most instances maintenance engineers should have adequate technical support from their headquarters staff. To provide this level of support service requires managerial commitment from the contractor, which may not always be forthcoming.

8.2.1 Periodic recommissioning

With some systems, monitoring may show a progressive deterioration of performance to a degree where recommissioning eventually becomes necessary. Where this can be shown to be due to ineffective maintenance, it would be reasonable to countercharge the maintenance contractor for a proportion of the recommissioning costs, provided that the terms of the contract made provision for this.

8.2.2 Control component influences

Design provisions can aid the maintenance task. For example, the provision of high quality sensors can reduce the tendency for set-point 'drift' and, thus, the need for regular recalibration. Also, intelligent controls can be arranged for self-monitoring; this can be a valuable asset in maintenance, provided that too much faith is not placed in this facility. The truly significant factor, however, is system performance and the maintenance engineer must always challenge and cross-check self-monitoring features. For example, the location of a monitoring sensor in a fluid distribution pipework or ductwork system can influence the reading and result in a misleading indication.

8.2.3 Contract performance monitoring

As with virtually all contracts, clients generally receive the service they demand or deserve. An unquestioning acceptance of the service, irrespective of the terms of the contract, tends to lead to a poor performance by the contractor. Where the client feels unable to monitor the level of maintenance service it should consider appointing an independent consultant to monitor the contractor's performance. This may be by way of a continuing formal routine of inspections or by *ad hoc* checks. Even here, it may be necessary for the client to guard against possible collusion between the contractor and the monitoring authority.

8.2.4 Contract options

The form and terms of the controls maintenance contract and the selection of the contractor can influence the maintenance performance. Examples of this include:

(*a*) manufacturer-based contracts: the contractor has an implicit incentive to ensure effective maintenance to support the reputation of that manufacturer's products and its specialist input to the controls system design

(*b*) contract maintenance: this arrangement includes full repairing responsibilities for a specified contract period and may also entail performance targets

(*c*) performance-related incentives: these are included in the terms of the contract and may be based on:

- energy consumption performance targeting
- for process applications, including computer room environmental systems, the consistent achievement of control parameters with penalties for deviation
- penalty clauses for control system failure or for other proven shortcomings
- incentives to rearrange maintenance schedules to minimise unnecessary service duties (e.g. 'shared' savings arrangements).

8.3 Routine maintenance checks

Primary responsibility for detailing the necessary routine checks of the controls system rests with the installation designer. In this role, it would be prudent to seek guidance from a controls specialist. The installation designer should also aim to identify and to highlight those controls that are most critical to the effective performance of the design.

The range and frequency of routine checks of controls will depend on the actual installation but useful indications of the necessary approach are provided in 'industry standard' publications such as the HVCA *Standard maintenance specification for mechanical services in buildings*[1]. Due account must also be taken of manufacturers' instructions but bear in mind that, for reasons of proprietary sensitivity, these may tend towards 'over maintenance'.

Typical controls checks include:

(*a*) the effective functioning of all safety devices (of primary importance)

(*b*) sensor set-point calibration, typically on a rolling programme basis, perhaps with more frequent checks on selected critical devices (see section 8.2)

(*c*) actuator functionality through the full operational range, with attention applied on a similar basis to (*b*).

The maintenance engineer should record salient details of routine checks in the system logbook in sufficient depth to permit the identification of recurring problems, trends or faults which are inclined to be typical. Where such records indicate a suspect component, this should be taken up with the manufacturer with a view to replacement by an improved design.

Where included in the maintenance specification, checks should be made on the energy consumption of the installation. Energy target limits should be set by the designer and, where measured performance falls outside these, some form of reporting and further investigation should be carried out.

As occupant satisfaction is one of the main aims of a control system, it would be reasonable for the client to consider the operation of a system of user reports compiled by the building occupants. Where appropriate, the user reports would be passed to the controls maintenance contractors for them to consider and recommend appropriate courses of action.

As with other aspects of maintenance and facilities management, the clients should consider routine review meetings with their controls maintenance team. These meetings would form part of the controls maintenance contract obligations and would normally be held at set intervals (say, quarterly or six-monthly) with provision for holding special meetings if required. The object of the meetings would be to monitor maintenance performance and to seek continuing improvement. Proceedings would generally be under the chairmanship of the client's premises manager and would be recorded by the maintenance contractor. Where independent maintenance contract performance monitoring is employed, the monitoring consultant should be present at review meetings and may undertake chairmanship on behalf of the client.

8.4 Building management systems

Although the system designer will have devised the controls concept which the building management system (BMS) is intended to fulfil, the designer may have only a limited understanding of how the actual BMS functions. A full understanding of the BMS is generally confined to the BMS manufacturer and it is not uncommon for a thorough understanding to be further limited to the specialists responsible for constructing the system software. It should be noted that industry standard algorithms for particular functions are available which can be adapted to suit a particular application. The extent to which the BMS manufacturer's maintenance team understands the system operation depends to a large degree on the quality of the back-up documentation provided by the installer.

Against this background, the level of faith typically placed in the effective functioning of a BMS may seem somewhat surprising. In principle, however, the effectiveness of a BMS depends directly and fundamentally on the software which it comprises. Furthermore, it is not unusual for BMS manufacturers to be cautious in disclosing details of their systems and software. The reasons stated for this generally concern commercial sensitivity.

Typically, the commissioning of a BMS is undertaken by the manufacturer. The degree of monitoring of this process which can be applied by the designer, the commissioning specialist or manager, or the witnessing authority will depend on their terms of appointment.

Maintenance of a BMS is also generally undertaken by the manufacturer. Access control by password may be arranged to permit varying levels of access for different personnel. Typically, ascending order of access would be arranged for the system operator, the controls specialist maintenance engineer and the controls specialist design team. As noted above, there is no guarantee that the BMS manufacturer's maintenance technicians will have a thorough understanding of the software. They can, however, reasonably be expected to be fully familiar with the hardware components used in the BMS installation.

As with all control systems, the effective functioning of any element will depend fundamentally on the correct location, positioning and calibration of the control sensor. Incorrect positioning or calibration will result in spurious readings which, arguably, may be less subject to challenge with a BMS than with conventional controls. This tendency results from the 'centralised' nature of the BMS which discourages maintenance checks and inspections at remote locations and relies on the 'monitoring' capability of the installation itself.

Ideally, the BMS maintenance engineer should retain a measure of scepticism regarding the capability of the system. To foster this approach, BMS maintenance routine schedules should include checks on control elements on a rolling programme basis. These should comprise checks of sensor location and calibration, ensuring that these are measuring true conditions and are not adversely influenced by fluid turbulence or incomplete mixing of fluid streams. Actuator operation should be checked over the complete control range movement. Most important of all, however, is the need to check the 'end result' of each control element — i.e. that the control is meeting its design intent efficiently and effectively.

The outcome of all these checks should be recorded in the BMS logbook, the entries being kept under continuing review by the maintenance engineer for indicative trends. Any indications such as deterioration in reliability of any components should be reported promptly to the client, together with supporting evidence, and acted upon as appropriate.

Energy consumption checks and recording or graphical plotting of control variables may be a suitable means of assessing the effectiveness of control performance.

Experienced controls maintenance technicians should be capable of assessing control effectiveness and, where appropriate, applying alternative technologies to do the job better. Back-up support from the BMS design office should be made available to undertake functions such as verifying the suitability of software algorithms.

8.5 Upgrading control systems

Developing technology tends to provide continuing opportunities for improvement of control systems, for example by enhanced capabilities of the system components or by improvements in the original concept. The cost effectiveness of any prospective improvement, however, should be assessed carefully by comparing the cost of the replacement control against the savings likely to be achieved by more efficient operation.

In most cases, the energy savings are likely to be marginal. To provide incentive for change, it may be necessary to make allowances based on the economic life expectancy of the existing control components. An exception to the 'marginal savings' case could be a proposal to install better quality sensors where existing units have been shown to suffer badly from set-point drift and thus to incur high labour costs for frequent recalibration. An independent consultant, where appointed, would be the logical arbiter to confirm any recommendation in respect of the viability of a replacement proposal, based on the consultant's knowledge of the controls system and its performance.

Another motivation for controls replacement could arise if the existing system proved to be too sophisticated, to an extent where it was not understood by the users and was too complex for the maintenance contractor to manage effectively. Such a situation would require a frank review, involving all the parties with an interest in the issue, taking account of all relevant factors and deciding on an appropriate course of action. Cost control of this action would be an important consideration. Again, an independent maintenance consultant, where appointed, would play an important part.

It is not uncommon for new technology to fall short of its initially predicted capabilities and performance. For this reason, the user should be cautious of revolutionary or 'panacea' proposals from the controls manufacturer or maintenance contractor. Even apparently successful track records in other applications may have limited relevance to the user's system. A prospective approach in this sort of instance would be for the user to be offered the enhancement on a payment-by-results basis. Clearly, it would be necessary to exercise care in drawing up the basis of a truly equitable means of assessing performance and any improvement.

The speed of development in the BMS field lends some credibility to the claim that a system is obsolescent the day after it is installed. Due to the cost of development, it is necessary for manufacturers to recoup these costs. This can lead to a tendency towards 'stepped' development rather than continuous improvement to provide a market for and an income from the existing BMS version. Where this policy is operated, the improvement between successive versions can be very marked. There may be some scope for users with an existing BMS to negotiate an arrangement with the proprietary supplier to provide version updates at reduced costs.

8.6 Need for training

The cyclic trends in the construction industry tend to result in periodic skill shortages in the various industry sectors. These workload peaks and troughs, combined with the time required for proper and effective technician training, make it difficult for an organisation to operate a training policy for its workforce. As a result, many arrangements for training are of an *ad hoc* nature. This, in turn, makes it difficult for customers to assess skill levels and to ensure that they are getting a 'fair deal' in respect of the competence of the labour dedicated to their work.

Controls manufacturers have an obligation to provide training in the installation, commissioning and maintenance of their own products for their own workforce. Some manufacturers also provide training for individuals other than their own personnel for the payment of a course fee. The duration of such training is dependent on the course objectives, but in most cases the coverage is confined to proprietary aspects of the company's own products and components, and delegates are expected to have existing control system knowledge and skills.

The low level of skills in some firms in the building engineering services sector of the construction industry has led to trade organisations introducing operative certification to provide some reassurance to customers (e.g. the welder's certificate operated by the Heating and Ventilating Contractors Association and the refrigerant handling certificate operated by the Air Conditioning and Refrigeration Industry Board. While there are no similar established schemes for controls maintenance personnel, it would be prudent for prospective customers to enquire at tender stage about the competence of the operative(s) to be dedicated to their work.

Note: it is a duty on employers under *The Construction (Design and Management) Regulations 1992*[(2)] to ensure that their personnel have the necessary competence and to provide them with appropriate training. Competence is particularly relevant to the maintenance of controls where the malfunction of a safety device could put building occupants at risk.

In addition to manual and craft skills it is important for a controls maintenance technician to have a good technical understanding of controls principles. Ideally, this knowledge should extend to an appreciation of controls concepts. Where the maintenance technician does not have this knowledge base, arrangements should be in place to provide ready access to technical back-up and the technicians encouraged to make proper use of this. Without this knowledge, the maintenance technician will be unable to effect improvements to the controls system and, indeed, would be unlikely to identify deterioration in controls system performance.

From the viewpoint of the controls maintenance contractor, the skills of its workforce are probably its major asset. In view of this, it is not unreasonable to expect the contractor to develop and promote these skills. The contractor should also recognise individual operative skills. In addition to continuing formal training, it is likely to be cost effective to provide staged opportunities for cross-fertilisation of skills and techniques between operatives. Innovations and suggestion schemes or other forms of incentives may offer appropriate means of deriving corporate benefit from this source.

It is implicit in the terms of any maintenance contract that the workforce will be skilled, experienced, properly trained and fully competent. It is, however, incumbent on the customers to monitor the service they receive and to ensure that the contract standards continue to be achieved. Where customers are unable to effect this monitoring from their own resources, it may be advantageous to retain the services of an independent expert to carry out assessments of contractual performance on their behalf.

References

1 *Standard maintenance specification for mechanical services in buildings: Volume 1: Heating and pipework systems* HVCA **SMG90** (1990); *Volume 2: Ventilating and air conditioning* HVCA **SMG90b** (1991); *Volume 3: Control, energy and building management systems* HVCA **SMG90c** (1992); *Volume 4: Ancillaries, plumbing and sewerage* HVCA **SMG90d** (1992); *Volume 5: Electrics in buildings* HVCA **SMG90e** (London: Heating and Ventilating Contractors Association) (dates as indicated)

2 *The Construction (Design and Management) Regulations 1994* Statutory Instrument 1994 No. 3140 (London: The Stationery Office) (1994)

9 Commissioning and testing

Contents

Summary

Reference is made to the scope of work of a commissioning specialist and the areas of involvement of a commissioning manager are described.

The need for comprehensive documentary support is stated and the various record requirements are outlined. The need to update records is noted.

The process of fine tuning the performance of an installation is outlined and details given of troubleshooting investigations and operational situations where repeat commissioning may be appropriate.

A designer's checklist for commissioning is provided and guidance on the decommissioning and mothballing of an installation given.

The commissioning and testing functions are defined and explained fully in the series of CIBSE Commissioning Codes(1–5).

— Commissioning is the advancement of an installation from static completion to working order according to specified requirements.

— Testing is the measurement and recording of system parameters to assess specification compliance.

All major projects should be assessed to see if there is justification for appointing a commissioning manager.

The responsibilities of the commissioning specialist can be extensive and various depending on how early the person is appointed and the extent of the brief. If appointed early enough, the commissioning specialist's input at the design stage can make a significant contribution to ensuring the success and timely completion of a project.

If the brief extends to a commissioning management role, the commissioning manager's responsibility is to interface all the works packages activities so as to produce complete operational systems on time. The commissioning manager should be appointed to the project/management team as early as possible so that the interfacing can happen in a proactive manner. The function of the commissioning manager is as a facilitator and catalyst bringing together diverse operations by cooperation, consensus and coordination and dealing with any or all the following:

(*a*) Electrical services:
  - high voltage and low voltage
  - uninterruptible power supply generators
  - security and fire systems
  - audio and information technology systems

(*b*) Mechanical services:
  - air and water systems
  - all mechanical plant

(*c*) Control systems:
  - lighting control systems
  - field controls and panels
  - building management systems
  - software

(*d*) Specialist equipment (normally commissioned by the equipment/system supplier):
  - lifts and escalators
  - sprinkler systems
  - car park barriers etc.
  - large refrigerating and boiler plant.

Terms of appointment vary, but the scope of works for a commissioning manager, which could apply to all the above for a complete project or to one specific element, could be:

(*a*) design review

(*b*) drawing review (including commissionability and maintainability)

(*c*) planning/programming for commissioning

(*d*) witnessing of works testing

(*e*) monitoring services installation against the specification and programme

(*f*) coordination of commissioning and maintenance documentation

(*g*) witnessing of site testing

(*h*) witnessing of the flushing and cleaning of pipework distribution systems

(*i*) witnessing of commissioning

(*j*) coordination of record documentation

(*h*) client training.

It must be emphasised that all installations, irrespective of size, need to be properly commissioned and the following general principles will apply. The appointed organisation must also have an awareness of the implications of *The Construction (Design and Management) Regulations 1994*[6] (CDM Regulations) and a policy and strategy for working to meet the regulations.

Commissioning specialist responsibilities may include some or all the following activities, depending on whether the appointment is for commissioning or for a wider commissioning management role.

(*a*) Design stage:

- review commissionability of design
- review maintainability of design
- review commissioning and testing content of specification.

(*b*) Post-design stage:

- produce project-specific commissioning and testing method statements
- prepare an integrated commissioning and testing programme.

(*c*) On-site duties:

- monitor and review installation in line with specified requirements
- coordinate, oversee and witness progressively the testing and commissioning
- monitor commissioning and testing programme and report progress
- collate test data
- oversee/coordinate production of operating and maintenance manuals and record drawings
- coordinate client training
- coordinate demonstrations of the safety systems to the local authorities, fire officer, district surveyor and building insurer.

Where the above duties are excluded from the terms of reference of the commissioning engineer, other suitably qualified members of the building services team must be delegated the appropriate responsibilities.

9.1 Documentation

Comprehensive documentation to support commissioning and testing activities is of paramount importance. Such records will show that statutory requirements have been met both mechanically and electrically allowing the building to be certified as safe for occupation.

Of much greater importance in the longer term, the commissioning documentation provides a record of the design operation of the commissioned systems. These records are invaluable in ensuring that the performance of the system is kept up to standard. Additionally, they provide an essential basis for the logical adjustment of system performance or for the recommissioning of systems following modifications or adaptations of the accommodation or its services.

It is essential that the completed documentation is kept safe and made readily available to everyone involved with the operation and maintenance of the building and its services. This documentation will form a permanent record and reference manual which interested parties can refer to ascertain the ongoing performance of the building services. It is essential that any changes, modifications or investigations carried out are undertaken in a controlled and logical manner and that a thorough audit trail of these events is kept with the original commissioning and testing records.

At practical completion, the following tabulated commissioning information should be available:

- main plant performance results
- air and water (flow regulation) results
- specialist plant commissioning/test results
- pipework and ductwork pressure test certificates
- fire alarm test certificate
- security/CCTV test certificates
- sprinkler/dry riser test and insurance certificates
- check-sheets recording systems interface
- check-sheets recording the commissioning of building management/ controls systems
- electrical completion and inspection certificate
- emergency lighting test certificate
- lightning protection test certificate
- test sheets recording the progressive testing of the electrical installation in accordance with *BS 7671*[7] (the IEE Regulations)
- chlorination certificate
- district surveyors' approvals
- statutory authorities' approvals
- as-fitted record drawings (indicating location of test points)
- operation and maintenance manuals
- flushing and cleaning, water treatment regimes.

Note: Commissioning documentation is considered to comprise part of the Health and Safety File required under the CDM Regulations[6].

9.2 Designer's checklist

The following checklist is applicable to all sizes of installations:

(*a*) Has the appointment of a commissioning specialist been considered?

(*b*) Can the systems be commissioned in accordance with the specification and the CIBSE Commissioning Codes[1–5]?

(*c*) Can the installed building services be adequately and safely maintained after handover?

(*d*) Have validation checks at manufacturer's works been allowed for on the major plant items?

(*e*) Have the patented systems been checked or tested rather than just assumed to be working

(*f*) Has sufficient detailed design information been provided, especially in respect of control regimes, including set-points, system flow rates and plant capacities?

(*g*) Is the specification definitive in its content of the commissioning responsibilities and acceptance criteria and tolerances?

(*h*) Is the specification adequately detailed in respect of the protection of plant and equipment during transportation, installation, commissioning and testing?

(i) Has a feedback procedure been implemented to recognise and address design problems that manifest during commissioning and testing in order to prevent repetition on future projects?

9.3 System characteristics

In the course of their work on a system, commissioning specialists learn a considerable amount about its operating characteristics. Commissioning specialists should be encouraged to include anecdotal notes on record documentation to highlight system characteristics and peculiarities which become apparent. Similarly, maintenance engineers should be encouraged to add written notes of their experiences in operating and servicing the system. In this way, documentation will be compiled on:

— accessibility

— modifications and/or upgrades to plant, equipment or systems

— system report

— system description

— experiences and observations made during periodic maintenance.

Such details often provide a valuable start point in a troubleshooting exercise.

9.4 Fine tuning

As defined earlier, the function of commissioning is to set a system into the required mode of operation, as envisaged by the designer. Fine tuning is the function of adjusting the operation of a commissioned system to match the actual need of the building occupier more closely. In certain instances this may include some form of remedial action to mitigate any adverse operational effects of overdesign (see section 5.3).

The design of a building services system is normally based on the interpretation of the client's requirements and a series of criteria assessments made by the designer. Inevitably, the specified parameters against which a system is commissioned do not generally coincide precisely with the actual operational requirements of the building occupier. The design provision may either exceed or underestimate the eventual requirements.

In the early stages of building occupation, these imbalances may lead to adjustments to flow rates in the air and water distribution systems to accommodate the occupier's requirements. The need for amendment to the flow rates should be assessed, the revised flow rates decided, appropriate adjustments made to the system and the actual modified flow rate measured and recorded. Additionally, the commissioning record documentation should be amended as necessary and, as with any installation modification, checks made to measure and record any effect on the remaining fluid distribution in the adjusted system.

Depending on the precise requirements of the occupants, the commissioning carried out to the original design may need to be readdressed if the final requirements differ from those envisaged in the initial design. This could justify a separate commissioning process to fine tune a system to match the occupant's specific needs.

If a building is designed as a speculative building and not bespoke for a particular client, there would be significant benefits in including a retuning commissioning process as part of the original installation contract or as a separate instruction issued subsequently. These benefits would include:

— in-built flexibility to meet a range of tenant needs

— reduction in post-contract problems evolving from inadequate control of environmental conditions

— reduced risk of the building user tampering with preset damper, grille, valve and control positions and settings affecting the system characteristics

— potential for cost savings due to accumulated site and systems knowledge.

9.5 Repeat testing and commissioning

There are a number of situations where repeat commissioning and testing/commissioning checks should be considered during the life of a building. These include:

— Changes of use within a building; these may result in physical modifications to a system and/or amendments to the design information which necessitates the proportional adjustment of air and/or water volume flow rates and the effect that this may have on central plant relative to fan/pump power consumption.

— A period of non-occupation and/or prolonged system shut-down (i.e. in excess of three months) depending on the complexity of the system and assuming that caretaker maintenance has been carried out during the shut down.

— Complaints from the building user regarding environmental conditions which, in turn, could result in a troubleshooting survey being required. This may indicate the need for aspects of the services installation to be recommissioned.

— A periodic validation: regular testing and recording of particular specified aspects of the performance of an installation.

— Following a periodic ductwork cleaning operation; for details refer to the HVCA's *Guide to good practice: cleanliness of ventilation systems*[8].

Each of the above situations requires different recommissioning techniques and logical approaches as detailed in the following sections.

Repeat commissioning or other means of system performance checks may indicate that plant and equipment are oversized for their required duty. Guidance on improving the operational performance of oversized plant is given in section 5.3.

9.5.1 Modifications to building services

Where there has been a change of use of a specific area within a building, it is important to consider the implications of local changes for the performance of the overall system. Where modifications are made to part of an air or water distribution system, the system characteristics may be affected and, consequently, the volume flow rates and power consumption of the fan/pump. Consideration should be given to modifying the fan or pump to better match the new performance requirement.

It is not possible to increase the flow rate to a particular area without reducing the flow by the same amount elsewhere in the system. Where an increased total flow rate is required, the fan or pump must be uprated or changed. Equally, where a reduced flow rate is required, the fan or pump must be downrated or changed. Any implications regarding electrical loads relative to the fans and pumps should be reviewed at the same time.

Local changes within variable air volume (VAV) systems may be less disruptive because the VAV terminals throughout the system will automatically self-compensate to a degree provided that they are not 'starved' of air or suffer significant reduction in static pressure.

When additions or changes are made to water distribution systems, it is important that the new pipework is thoroughly flushed and cleaned before being connected to the main system. Corrosion inhibition should also be considered as any new pipework or components would be more vulnerable to corrosion than the existing system.

The designer responsible for changes to an existing system would benefit from discussing the proposals with a commissioning specialist. Such discussion would take account of the existing commissioning records and would facilitate any recommissioning which may be necessary.

9.5.2 Non-occupation or system shutdown

If a building has been unoccupied but properly commissioned and caretaker maintenance provided, allowing water systems to be circulated and air plant to be 'spun over' at regular intervals, the services should continue to operate efficiently and air and water volume flow rates should remain in balance. This can be checked by comparing random air and water flow rates or fan/pump power consumption with the original commissioning data.

It is important that any prospective tenant or building user carries out a health and safety risk assessment for the recommissioned premises before the mechanical and electrical services are inspected and recommissioned. The inspection should ensure that the services are in good safe working condition prior to being run up and demonstrate that they are operating and performing correctly and efficiently.

This can be achieved by confirming that the documentation is in place, visually inspecting the installation and undertaking random tests to ensure that the services have remained as originally commissioned. Water samples should be taken at various locations in hydraulic systems and sent for analysis to check water quality including the iron/mineral content as an indication of the suitability of corrosion inhibitor treatment levels. With all open water systems, biological analysis should be undertaken to check for health hazards e.g. legionellosis. This would, as a minimum, include condenser cooling water, and hot and cold water services systems.

A full report, written in layman's terms. should be issued to the prospective tenant summarising the findings of the survey and recommendations for recommissioning.

9.5.3 Troubleshooting

In the event of complaints or suspicion of incorrect operation of the services within a building, the cause should be investigated. It is important not to be too hasty in drawing conclusions. A logical, systematic approach is essential to ensure any recommended remedial works are directed at the true source of the problem and do not make the situation worse. Before the investigation starts, the following should be undertaken:

— check that the original commissioning and testing records are available

— check that the services have been maintained correctly

— listen to the occupants

— talk to the building user and consider the complaint

— check the status of systems and undertake preliminary tests

— consider how the services are designed to operate (an overview) and what particular problems may have led to the situation being experienced

— review control functions and set-points and check their correct operation.

Only when the above course of action has been followed and preliminary tests carried out can a suitable solution and a corrective action approach be decided. Assume nothing; only preliminary testing will provide definitive evidence of flow rates, temperatures etc.

It is not possible to recommend a common approach to troubleshooting. What is most important is that the engineer leading the investigation is able to maintain an overview of the systems and understands how the systems were intended to operate and to interact to achieve the required environmental conditions within the building.

Any alterations or modifications made as a result of these investigations must be fully documented and the commissioning records and operation and maintenance manuals revised accordingly.

9.5.4 Periodic validation

The requirement for periodic system validation will depend on a number of factors from the building use to commercial considerations. Within the pharmaceutical industry, regular validation checks as part of good maintenance are now mandatory under the requirements of the US Food and Drug Administration.

With the growing concern and increasing statutory requirements for providing a healthy working and process environment, regular checks should be undertaken to ensure that buildings and services systems remain within the operational state required by the occupier. To achieve this a schedule of routine tests of building services should be set up as part of the planned preventive maintenance regime. Where appropriate, fine tuning should be undertaken and an audit trail kept of any changes made.

As an installation operational history is built up, changes in the system performance will become readily apparent and an optimum frequency of validation tests will evolve.

9.6 Controls and building management systems

The commissioning specialist and the controls commissioning engineer need to liaise at the earliest possible stage in a project to agree an integrated programme and ensure that the necessary interface between the two disciplines is agreed as early as possible. Both will need each other to bring a system forward to a point where it can be advanced or completed. Furthermore, both will need exclusive time on a system with no interference from others.

Close liaison is imperative for the protection of the system components. More important, however, is the need for the engineers to cooperate fully with one another when safety systems are being brought to operational status.

See also section 8.4 for guidance on maintenance of building management systems.

9.7 Decommissioning and mothballing

Decommissioning and mothballing are two distinctly different processes, and the precise requirements of the client in respect of the building need to be established before detailing a plan of action. Each building will need to be assessed individually.

9.7.1 Decommissioning

This is the systematic process of isolating, draining down water systems, and purging all mechanical and electrical plant and equipment, including specialist plant and equipment and services (lifts, escalators, medical gases, fume cupboards etc.). This should be carried out through a planned sequence of events supported by method statements and permit-to-work procedures, as appropriate.

The decommissioning may be carried out as part of the process to demolish the building or to carry out a large-scale refurbishment. Alternatively, its purpose may be to render the building eligible to be zero-rated by the local authority. This may be achieved by following the above process, plus disconnecting certain plant to a point such that the building is rendered 'incapable of beneficial occupation' and would require an unreasonable amount of expenditure to make it suitable for re-occupation.

However, there are other considerations and implications that need to be taken in to account including:

(*a*) interrelationship of the building services with neighbouring premises

(*b*) integrity of the fire, security and safety systems

(*c*) provision of temporary lighting and emergency lighting on staircases and hazardous walkways

(*d*) possible retention of an in-service lift (which may be prudent in high-rise buildings)

(*e*) possible need to maintain in running order essential plant and equipment, e.g. sump pumps, sewage ejectors, sprinkler pumps, dry riser or ventilation plant.

9.7.2 Mothballing

This is the preparation of the building services to provide only essential environmental requirements in an unoccupied or unlet building. This would include frost protection, fire, security and safety features to maintain the safety and integrity of the building, and minimising the input required to restore all services to full running order. A caretaker maintenance regime will need to be set up to turn moving parts and run specific items of plant periodically.

Mothballing enables the client to:

(*a*) benefit from the local authority unoccupied property rate (50% of normal office rates)

(*b*) minimise running costs

(*c*) save energy

(*d*) maintain the building in a state of readiness to meet a change in circumstances promptly.

References

1 *Air distribution systems* CIBSE Commissioning Code A (London: Chartered Institution of Building Services Engineers) (1996)

2 *Boiler plant* CIBSE Commissioning Code B (London: Chartered Institution of Building Services Engineers) (1975)

3 *Automatic controls* CIBSE Commissioning Code C (London: Chartered Institution of Building Services Engineers) (1973)

4 *Refrigerating systems* CIBSE Commissioning Code R (London: Chartered Institution of Building Services Engineers) (1991)

5 *Water distribution systems* CIBSE Commissioning Code W (London: Chartered Institution of Building Services Engineers) (1994)

6 *The Construction (Design and Management) Regulations 1994* Statutory Instrument 1994 No. 3140 (London: Stationery Office) (1994)

7 *BS 7671: 1992: Requirements for electrical installations. IEE Wiring Regulations. Sixteenth edition* (London: British Standards Institution) (1992)

8 *Guide to good practice: cleanliness of ventilation systems* HVCA Technical Report **TR/17** (London: Heating and Ventilating Contractors Association) (1998)

Bibliography

Parsloe C *The commissioning of water systems in buildings* BSRIA Application Guide **AG2/89.2** (Bracknell: Building Services Research and Information Association) (1998)

Parsloe C *The commissioning of air systems in buildings* BSRIA Application Guide **AG3/89.2** (Bracknell: Building Services Research and Information Association) (1998)

Commissioning of VAV systems in buildings services BSRIA Application Guide **AG1/91** (Bracknell: Building Services Research and Information Association) (1991)

Parsloe C *Pre-commission cleaning of water systems* BSRIA Application Guide **AG8/91** (Bracknell: Building Services Research and Information Association) (1991)

Wild L J *Commissioning HVAC systems — division of responsibilities* BSRIA Technical Memoranda **TM1/88** (Bracknell: Building Services Research and Information Association) (1988)

Pike P and Pennycook K *Commissioning of BEMS — a code of practice* BSRIA **AH/2/92** (Bracknell: Building Services Research and Information Association) (1992)

Nanayakkara R *The CDM regulations health and safety file* BSRIA Application Guide **AG7/97** (Bracknell: Building Services Research and Information Association) (1997)

Gill P The art of constructive vandalism (decommissioning) *Building Services* **15**(11) 33–35 (1993)

Standard specification for the commissioning of mechanical engineering services installations for buildings (Horsham: Commissioning Specialists Association) (1999)

10 Handover procedures

Contents

Summary

The various activities which become relevant as handover approaches are listed, the need to make preparations for this is noted and a typical checklist provided. The importance of commissioning is discussed and the necessary arrangements for inspecting the works, including inspections required by statute, are outlined.

Provisions for user demonstrations and training are recommended and arrangements for the handover of tools, spares and keys for the services installations are referred to.

The typical contents of a handover information pack are detailed and guidance is given on defects liability and equipment warranties.

The option of phased handover and the advantages to the client of beneficial occupation are briefly described.

Handover follows on from project completion which is the point in the construction process when the architect or project manager determines that the building is, to all intents and purposes, complete and ready for the client. Once completion has been certified, the contractor gives up occupation of the site to the client who takes over responsibility for security, insurance, operation and maintenance. The other contractual actions normally triggered by completion are:

- commencement of the defects liability period
- release of a proportion of the construction contract retention fund
- commencement of the architect's final review
- opening of any reference to arbitration
- cessation of the contractor's liability for liquidated damages
- cessation of the contractor's liability for subsequent frost damage.

In practical terms, the handover of building services systems is a gradual process, involving numerous inspections, user demonstrations and witnessing of commissioning and tests. The main parties involved will, typically, be the mechanical and electrical contractor(s), the designer and the client's maintenance personnel or nominated maintenance contractor. Good communication is especially important during the final stages of construction; ideally the maintenance personnel or contractor should be involved early in the handover process.

10.1 Preparation

General preparations for the handover proceedings are coordinated and supervised continuously by the architect/project manager in close liaison with the other members of the design team. While the events surrounding handover occur at the end of the construction process, a coordinated programme of activities should be drawn up well in advance to help ensure minimal complications. A programme of pre-handover activities should be agreed, including allocating responsibility for all inspections and the issuing of certificates.These activities can then be monitored and controlled.

The pre-handover checklist below may assist in creating such a programme of activities. The relevance, timing and responsibility for carrying out the activities will be determined by the nature of the project and associated contracts.

10.1.1 Pre-handover checklist

10.1.1.1 Two–three months before completion

Approximately two to three months before the scheduled completion date it should be ensured that:

- the client is informed of any likelihood of change to the scheduled completion date
- contractual obligations regarding witnessing of commissioning and testing, failure defect and deficiency inspections and outstanding items of work (snagging) are clarified
- the client is made fully aware of its post-handover obligations including the need to arrange insurances and contracts for maintenance
- arrangements are made to recruit operation and maintenance personnel as required
- relevant authoritative bodies have been approached to determine any necessary inspections/approvals; this may include the local authority, the Health and Safety Executive and the fire authority

- the client is consulted regarding the format and required procedures for the handover meeting
- pre-commissioning cleaning of the heating, ventilating and air-conditioning systems is carried out
- tariffs for the utility supplies have been negotiated and a contract with a meter operator arranged
- the planning supervisor has issued general details of the structure's equipment, maintenance facilities and procedures, construction methods and materials for inclusion in the Health and Safety File
- inspection of works commences in accordance with inspection policy and programme.

10.1.1.2 One month before completion

Approximately one month before the scheduled completion date it should be ensured that:

- if required, an engineer is appointed to assist the client during the initial period of occupation
- licences are obtained for the storage of hazardous chemicals
- draft operation and maintenance manual and record drawings are submitted and checked
- ongoing inspections are carried out in accordance with inspection policy
- a schedule of any outstanding work is agreed
- any additional works that are required are arranged
- all necessary statutory examinations have taken place (fire systems, means of escape, pressure systems and lifts)
- all utility supplies are inspected, approved and signed off
- user demonstrations and training session(s) have taken place, details recorded of those in attendance and certificates of competence awarded, as appropriate.

10.1.1.3 One week before completion

Approximately one week before completion it should be ensured that:

- all commissioning work has been completed and witnessed
- the commissioning report(s) and associated information have been issued
- all the required test certificates have been issued
- final inspections have been completed as required
- water treatment appropriate to the installed services has been carried out
- all warranty documentation has been issued
- the completed/semi-complete operation and maintenance manuals and record drawings have been issued and approved
- all the required tools, spares, consumables etc. have been assembled, and an inventory provided
- waste/surplus materials been removed from the site
- the Health and Safety File has been checked and issued
- re-lamping, filter changing and cleaning have taken place as required by the specification
- the listed outstanding defects have been rectified to acceptable standards
- all meter readings and fuel stocks have been recorded.

10.2 Commissioning

At the pre-contract stage, the design team should identify the services which must be commissioned and divide responsibility for carrying out the work between the contractor and the manufacturers or suppliers. Statutory and insurance approvals must also be identified and responsibility assigned for obtaining them. Adequate provision must be included in the contract for carrying out commissioning, including requirements for witnessing test results, and the production of commissioning information and reports to the specified format.

At the start of commissioning, the designer should ensure that a full programme of work is available. While the services may be fully installed and ready for commissioning, consideration should be given as to how any incomplete building work might affect testing, e.g. missing doors may influence air distribution system balancing.

Any failure of a system to achieve the specified design duty appropriate to the time of year that commissioning is taking place should be reported promptly by the commissioning specialist. Wherever possible, apparent or contributory reasons should be indicated in the report. It is the designer's prerogative to consider how the implications of such a failure might affect the operation of the building. This will depend on the degree of any performance shortfall and the designer's analysis of the reasons behind it. Action to remedy the situation need not delay completion unless the fault is serious.

Commissioning tests should be witnessed by the designer and main contractor in accordance with the contract. The final acceptance of the system will depend on how the actual commissioned performances compare with the specified duties and related tolerances.

All commissioning information and related documentation must be kept safely. This includes any pre-commissioning reports and checklists. Ideally, the information should form a distinct section in the operation and maintenance manual and a provision to this effect can be included in the manual specification. Commissioning information is often helpful in resolving system performance problems and any disputes that may occur during the defects liability period.

10.3 Inspections

From a building services perspective, completion requires that, except for very minor items, all systems are installed and commissioned in accordance with the works contract. Any outstanding items must not pose a health and safety risk or interfere with the operation of the engineering system to which they relate. Furthermore, they should cause no more than very minor disruption to the activities of the building operator. The client can help to ensure that this requirement is satisfied by indicating to the architect/project manager any items of particular importance to its business which must not be outstanding at completion.

Typically, the design team will have a contractual duty to undertake a final inspection of the works for deficiencies and defects before completion. This will be preceded by a comprehensive inspection by the installing contractors and subcontractors. To help ensure that inspections can be conducted effectively, an inspection policy should be drawn up between all parties detailing the standards that must be achieved, the sequence of inspections and any specific access requirements.

10.3.1 Defect status sheet

The use of a defect status sheet will help keep track of outstanding items and enable rectification to be prioritised as appropriate but particularly where there are health and safety implications. The defects status sheet can take the form of a simple table with columns for:

— inspected item

— location

— date of inspection

— description of defect

— responsibility for rectification

— date of defect clearance

— date of re-inspection.

10.3.2 Statutory inspections

There is a legal obligation for lifting equipment and pressure systems to undergo a statutory examination before they are put into service. These examinations must be carried out by a competent person who will typically be a surveyor from a specialist insurance or maintenance organisation. Further examinations of the lifts and lifting equipment are required at regular intervals.

The frequency of pressure system examinations will be specified in a written scheme of examination drawn up by a pressure systems examiner based on the conditions of use. Pressure vessels such as boilers and air receivers will undergo an initial examination at their place of manufacture and will be dispatched with the appropriate certification. This does not, however, preclude a further site examination by a competent person.

10.4 User training

If it is the client's intention to outsource all or part of the maintenance, arrangements for training should be made well in advance of handover to ensure attendance of the maintenance contractor. Where the client intends to use in-house resources for operation or maintenance, the appropriate personnel must be nominated, their responsibilities clarified and arrangements made to ensure their attendance.

Training sessions with a significant technical content should be divided into two parts. The first part should be in a classroom environment where a systems overview can be provided and the format of the operation and maintenance manual explained. The second part should be a tour of the building to allow specific elements of the engineering systems to be identified and their operation demonstrated. Wherever possible, opportunities for hands-on experience should be provided for the trainees. When planning training sessions, thought should be given to the number of contact hours required in the classroom and on-site for each system. Consideration should also be given to practical requirements such as classroom size, visual presentation equipment, and training documentation and schematics.

It may also be advisable to make provision for the training sessions to be recorded on video. This would provide a visual account of operating procedures which can enhance the information provided by the operation and maintenance manual and assist in the training of future operators or the arrangement of refresher courses.

The client will need to ensure that, where applicable, designated personnel within the organisation attend the training session(s) and a record is kept of the attendees, including details of any certificates of competence issued. Where relevant, a record should be kept of individuals' appointed responsibilities for specific systems, e.g. authorised personnel for high voltage and water systems, and competent persons for pressure systems and lifting equipment etc.

10.5 Tools, spares and keys

Provisions may have been included in the contract for the supply of spares and specialist tools. Checks must be made to ensure that these have been provided by the contractor and that all items are accounted for.

Specialist tools and spares should be suitably packaged to prevent corrosion or damage and be easily identifiable. Examples of specialist tools include bearing extractors, alignment jigs and calibration equipment.

A complete description of all the spares should be provided including, where appropriate:

— drawing number

— item and part number

— details of size and type

— manufacturer's name and reference number for all items supplied by a specialist manufacturer.

Where required, clean air filters must be fitted and a check made to see that this has been carried out and that the appropriate number of spare filters is provided.

If re-lamping is specified as a contractual requirement, checks should be made to ensure that it has been carried out satisfactorily. If re-lamping is not required, an estimation of the hours of beneficial usage may be needed so that a cash settlement can be agreed between the contractor and client. Alternatively, the contractor may be required to provide a specific number of spare lamps. (All such requirements must be detailed in the contract specification.)

The contractor should produce a key schedule before handover and ensure that it is up to date when it is passed to the client. The schedule should be comprehensive, include a unique code for key identification and details of their availability on site.

10.6 Handover information

Requirements for handover information will need to be agreed well in advance of the expected date of completion and will need to take account of individual responsibilities for producing information and dates for the completion of specific items including drafts that require approval. The building services contractor is usually responsible for coordinating the handover information for building services.

The majority of the information passed to the client at handover will form part of the Health and Safety File as required by the CDM Regulations(1) (see section 18.8 for further guidance).

BSRIA Technical Note TN15/95 *Handover information for building services*(2) contains comprehensive guidance on the broad range of documentation and drawings that should be provided at handover. This includes a checklist of the certificates and documentation that building owners and operators must have in their possession before they can legally operate the building. Detailed guidance on specifying and procuring operation and maintenance manuals is provided in BSRIA Application Guide AG1/87.1 *Operating and maintenance manuals for building services installations*(3), which includes a model specification and details of contractual arrangements; see section 11.

10.7 Equipment warranties

Equipment warranties normally run from the date of delivery or from the date when the equipment is first operated. The latter is particularly useful in situations where the time span between purchasing the equipment and handover is likely to be significantly protracted. Where cover is required beyond the standard period, an extended warranty can usually be arranged through payment of an additional premium to the supplier and ensuring that appropriate storage protection is provided and operational requirements are satisfied. The precise terms of a warranty can often be tailored to suit the particular needs of the client.

To ensure that a warranty remains valid, it is essential that the equipment is maintained in accordance with the supplier's instructions or other specified requirements. Before completion, this will be the responsibility of the installation contractor; following completion, responsibility passes to the client unless specific contractual arrangements have been made for the contractor to continue maintaining the plant. A comprehensive record of all maintenance work should be kept. Where equipment failures occur, lengthy disputes may ensue between the supplier, contractor and engineering consultant regarding the cause of the failure, i.e. whether it resulted from a fault within the equipment, the way it was operated or by features of the system which it serves. To resolve such disputes as quickly as possible, it can be beneficial for all parties to meet on site to review the failure and, if possible, reach some form of agreement regarding the cause.

10.8 Sectional completion and beneficial occupation

Sectional completion (also referred to as phased handover) is the term given to distinct phases of the works being completed sequentially where provision is made for this in the contract. The purpose of including such a provision is to allow the client to occupy a particular area (or areas) prior to practical completion so that specific equipment and services relating to the client's business can be installed without delay. As the contract provides for sectional completion, consent from the contractor is not required before the client takes up occupation. As each phase of the works is completed, a certificate of section completion is issued. Only one certificate of practical completion is issued for the complete contract.

Beneficial occupation (also referred to as partial possession) is the term given to early occupation of the works by the client where the contract does not include a specific provision for this. The consent of the contractor is required since, contractually, it has exclusive possession of the site until practical completion is reached. The contractor is likely to require financial compensation for the inconvenience that beneficial occupation will cause. It is also likely that a certificate of partial possession will be issued for the occupied area. This has the same contractual significance as practical completion, triggering the commencement of the defects liability period, the client's responsibility for operation and maintenance, and the release of part of the retention fund.

10.9 Defects liability

While many of the defects that occur after handover can be corrected towards the end of the defects liability period some may require immediate attention. An arrangement between the client and contractor for dealing with such defects should be established in advance of handover so that they can be rectified with minimal delay.

It is important that the client keeps a detailed record of any work carried out by the contractor(s) during the defects liability period in case of any subsequent disputes. This record should include details of:

- nature of the defect(s)
- any consequent or subsequent damage to other plant and systems resulting from the defect(s)
- correspondence between client and contractor
- action taken by contractor
- dates of all events, actions and correspondence
- details of maintenance work carried out.

It should be noted that failure on the client's part to ensure that the building services are operated and maintained in an effective manner during the defects liability period may reduce the responsibility of the contractor to make good latent defects.

When the end of the defects liability period is reached — typically one year after completion — the final account details can be agreed, including the adjustment of prime costs, provisional sums and variations. When all listed outstanding defects have been made good, the remainder of the retention fund is released and the final certificate issued. At this point, the right of both parties to pursue new claims comes to an end with the exception of further claims relating to defects. Liability for defects normally runs for a period of six years from the date of completion (see section 4.5.11).

An organisation procuring a building for business use has good protection afforded against defective building performance by the contract. However, owners/occupiers who are not responsible for building procurement will not have any form of contractual relationship with the architect or consulting engineer and will consequently need to protect themselves against financial loss resulting from defects which may appear in the structure or building services after completion. An example of this would be tenants with full repairing liabilities and organisations that purchase buildings from property developers.

For building services systems, this protection is likely to take the form of a collateral warranty which will be a contract between the consulting engineer, who is the warrantor, and the recipient, who is the warrantee. The warranty can either be in the form of a 'simple contract' which allows the injured party to sue up to six years after the breach of contract or a 'contract under seal' for which the period is extended to 12 years (see section 4.1.3). Consulting engineers should never enter into a collateral warranty contract without first carefully checking the terms of their professional indemnity insurance and ensuring that these are compatible.

An alternative to collateral warranties is latent defects insurance which does not require the recipient to prove negligence or breach of contract, enabling cover to be provided on a 'no fault basis'. Sources of further reading on the subject of warranties and insurance are included in the bibliography.

References

1 *The Construction (Design and Management) Regulations 1994* Statutory Instrument 1994 No. 3140 (London: Stationery Office) (1994)

2 de Saulles T *Handover information for building services* BSRIA Technical Note **TN15/95** (Bracknell: Building Services Research and Information Association) (1995)

3 Armstrong J H *Operating and maintenance manuals for building services installations* BSRIA Application Guide **AG1/87.1** (Bracknell: Building Services Research and Information Association) (1990)

Bibliography

Air distribution systems CIBSE Commissioning Code A (London: Chartered Institution of Building Services Engineers) (1996)

Boiler plant CIBSE Commissioning Code B (London: Chartered Institution of Building Services Engineers) (1975)

Automatic controls CIBSE Commissioning Code C (London: Chartered Institution of Building Services Engineers) (1973)

Refrigerating systems CIBSE Commissioning Code R (London: Chartered Institution of Building Services Engineers) (1991)

Water distribution systems CIBSE Commissioning Code W (London: Chartered Institution of Building Services Engineers) (1994)

Preparation of operating and maintenance documentation for building systems ASHRAE Guideline 4 (Atlanta GA: American Society of Heating, Refrigeration and Air Conditioning Engineers) (1993)

Parsloe C *Allocation of design responsibilities for building engineering services — a code of conduct to avoid conflict* BSRIA Technical Note **TN21/97** (Bracknell: Building Services Research and Information Association) (1997)

Parsloe C *Allocation of design responsibilities for building engineering services — example drawings* BSRIA Technical Note **TN22/97** (Bracknell: Building Services Research and Information Association) (1997)

Planning to build? A practical introduction to the construction process CIRIA Special Publication **113** (London: Construction Industry Research and Information Association) (1995)

Code of practice for project management for construction and development (Ascot: Chartered Institute of Building) (1996)

Architect's job book (London: Royal Institute of British Architects) (1996)

Cornes D L *Design liability in the construction industry* (Oxford: Blackwell Scientific) (1996)

11 Operation and maintenance manuals

Contents

Summary

The constituent parts suggested in the BSRIA Application Guide AG1/87 are presented as a suitable basis for operation and maintenance manuals. The need for manufacturers to provide clear, explicit and relevant instructions is noted.

Mention is made of the scope for using an electronic format for manuals and the ease of extending this into a computer-based maintenance management system.

The relevance of the manual as a day-to-day working document is noted and the need for it to be readily available for use is stressed.

The Construction (Design and Management) Regulations 1994[1] (CDM Regulations) and, in particular, the requirement for the Health and Safety File have tended to raise the profile of and need for high-quality operation and maintenance manuals and record drawings (see section 18.7).

The HSE's approved code of practice[2] gives further guidance on the information contained in the Health and Safety File as follows:

'Information contained in the file needs to include that which assists persons carrying out construction work on the structure at any time after completion of the current project and may include:

(*a*) record or 'as built' drawings and plans used and produced throughout the construction process along with the design criteria

(*b*) general details of the construction methods and materials used

(*c*) details of the structure's equipment and maintenance facilities

(d) maintenance procedures and requirements for the structure

(*e*) manuals produced by specialist contractors and suppliers which outline operating and maintenance procedures and schedules for plant and equipment installed as part of the structure

(*f*) details on the location and nature of utilities and services, including emergency and fire-fighting systems.'

The BSRIA Application Guide AG1/87.1 *Operation and maintenance manuals for building services installations*[3] provides detailed guidance on the content and quality of operation and maintenance manuals and will generally satisfy the requirements of the CDM Regulations.

11.1 Content

The presentation of information within the manual does not need to follow a rigid format but should cover the range of topics listed in BSRIA AG 1/87.1[3]. All manuals, however small, should contain a contents list and a comprehensive index. AG 1/87.1 suggests the following presentation of information:

- How to use the manual
- Contractual and legal duties
- Overall purpose (including design parameters)
- System descriptions, including control concepts
- Equipment schedules and reference numbers
- Spares policy and recommended spares lists
- Commissioning records and data
- Operation instructions
- Maintenance instructions
- Modification information
- Disposal instructions
- Record drawing schedules (including the location of the drawings)
- Emergency information
- Manufacturers' literature relevant to the installation (including directory of names and addresses).

Part 2 of AG1/87.1 also gives recommendations on the depth of detail required when preparing operation and maintenance manuals and should be consulted as the standard reference work. The recommended depth of detail required for preparing record drawings is covered in Appendix 3 of AG1/87.1, and again this should be taken as the standard reference. The use of photographs in operation and maintenance manuals is encouraged as they show the progressive stages of the installation and any hidden services.

11.2 Manufacturers' literature

It is recommended that the provision of clear and unambiguous record documentation by the manufacturer is made a specific requirement at the design stage. Additionally, it should be made a condition when placing orders that explicit and specific operation and maintenance instructions for the item of equipment be supplied. This will avoid the issuing of basic and general literature covering ranges and types of equipment other than that supplied. It should also be a condition that date stamped and certified 'as built' drawings are provided, together with recommended spares lists and disposal instructions. Manufacturer's literature and certified 'as built' drawings may both be available in electronic format should this be preferred.

11.3 Computer-based information systems

The use of computer technology enables most, if not all, of an operation and maintenance manual to be presented in electronic format. These computer-based systems provide a direct replacement for hard-copy manuals, and allow the user to view text and graphics on-screen. Several systems make use of sophisticated software tools which allow the user to navigate around documents by links or user-definable searches. This can help overcome the problem of handling and searching large amounts of information.

It is also possible to incorporate direct links to computer aided design (CAD) record drawings, building energy management system (BEMS) graphics, word-processed control strategies, and word-processed testing and commissioning results. CAD-prepared record drawings are convenient for preparing, storing, updating and viewing part or whole areas of building services installations. This flexibility, however, should not be allowed to override the importance of recording full details of any changes to drawings.

Computer-based information systems offer the option to print all or selected sections of the operating and maintenance manual in a hard copy format.

11.4 Maintenance management systems

An obvious advantage of well-produced record documentation to the end user of a building services installation will be the ease of transferring the documentation into a building maintenance management system. This provides an automated method of planning, controlling, recording, costing and monitoring operation and maintenance activities during the life of the installation.

11.5 Updating

There has always been a need to update documents and the introduction of the CDM Regulations [1] (see also section 18) includes a duty to update documents during the life of the installation. The updates should also take into account knowledge gained through operational experience.

This was previously highlighted by a recommendation in the Badenoch Report 1986[4] and in *BS 8210*[5]. Paragraph 3.4.4 of *BS 8210* states: 'The value of maintenance guides depends on the degree to which they are kept up to date. When changes occur to the building concerned or when new information becomes available, all copies of the maintenance guides should be amended, and they should be reviewed annually.'

Furthermore, the *Health and Safety at Work etc. Act*[6], paragraph 2.1.c, refers to the duty of every employer in: 'The provision of such information, instruction, training and supervision as is necessary to ensure, so far as is reasonably practicable, the health and safety at work of his employees.' This can be interpreted as requiring the regular updating of manuals to include details of all modifications to plant and systems as and when they occur.

11.6 Preparation

The requirement and responsibility for producing the operation and maintenance manuals may well justify the engagement of a specialist organisation with the requisite engineering and information technology skills to produce high quality comprehensive documentation to an appropriate quality standard.

Under the CDM Regulations[1] the client has a statutory requirement to make sure the Health and Safety File (and thus the operation and maintenance manuals) are kept secure and ready for inspection by any person who may need access to the information. It is important, therefore, that the client considers how the information should be prepared and managed as well as appointing responsibility for revisions (see also section 18.7).

Working copies should be kept of all important documentation. The originals (including a copy of the operation and maintenance manual) must be kept in a safe location, preferably off-site.

References

1 *The Construction (Design and Management) Regulations 1994* (London: The Stationery Office) (1994)

2 *Managing construction for health and safety: Construction (Design and Management) Regulations 1994. Approved code of practice* HSE **L54** (Sudbury: Health and Safety Executive) (1995)

3 Armstrong J H *Operation and maintenance manuals for building services installations* BSRIA Application Guide **AG1/87.1** (Bracknell: Building Services Research and Information Association) (1990)

4 Badenoch J (ch.) Second report of the Committee of Inquiry into the outbreak of Legionnaires' Disease in Staffordshire in 1985 (London: The Stationery Office) (1986)

5 *BS 8210: 1986 Guide to building maintenance management* (London: British Standards Institution) (1986)

6 *Health and Safety at Work etc. Act 1974* (London: The Stationery Office) (1974)

12 Risk assessment procedures

Contents

Summary

The range of risks that require assessment are divided into four categories.

Business risks affecting the operation of an enterprise are discussed and range from loss of a building service to an act of God.

Design and installation risks are detailed and the need for design standards, standby plant and equipment, and the relevance of insurance provisions are dealt with.

Operation and maintenance risks in the early stages of a new installation, together with warranties and the liability for defects and risks in an ongoing operation, are considered.

Risks associated with the disposal of obsolete plant or equipment that has reached the end of its economic life are outlined.

Risk can be defined as the chance or possibility of loss or bad consequences, or the possibility of incurring misfortune or loss. For all but the most basic buildings, the built environment relies to a large extent on the building services engineering installations. The risks associated with these installations have to be assessed at all stages, from concept to dismantling and disposal. This is to ensure that the risks are acceptable within the parameters defined by the overall requirements, statutory obligations and good practice.

Organisations depend on building services for lighting and power for every day working, and for ventilation and air conditioning to provide comfortable conditions and support critical processes. The risks to production or personal well-being associated with these systems are usually assumed to be minimal and the full implications are often not appreciated until something goes wrong. Failure will not always be due to bad design, installation, operation or maintenance. The effects of a breakdown can range from inconvenience, as in the case of an overloaded circuit to a photocopier, to loss of life or the destruction of a building.

Risks can be classified into categories, according to the area they derive from or affect:

- business: those risks that help to determine the specification for the building engineering service
- design and installations: those risk that have to be considered when looking at the options for design and installation
- operation and maintenance: those risks involved in running the plant and equipment
- disposal: risks that are likely to be similar to the operation and maintenance risks but worth considering separately.

Table 12.1 summarises the risks associated with each of the four categories, Figure 12.1 provides a standard format for a risk assessment, and Figure 12.2 provides a chart for identifying the results of a risk assessment.

12.1 Business risks

12.1.1 Defining the operation, process or business

Business risks are related to the type of operation carried out by the organisation and will influence the final design of the building services.

Examples of higher risk operations are: continuous manufacturing processes, hospital operating theatres, broadcasting networks, computer centres, finance house dealing rooms, communications facilities and transportation systems. In air traffic control, for example, the overall reliability required may be higher than 99.9% and the mean time between failures (MTBF) for the building services will therefore need to be of the same order as the computer equipment providing the service. The risk to life may be the highest priority in some of these examples, but all will include some measure of financial risk, either direct or consequential.

Some parts of the operation will be more critical to the overall risk to the business than others, and will often be time related. For example, production delays will represent a greater risk in the short term than personnel delays, although the loss of a critical personnel function on a continuing basis might be just as damaging to the business in the longer term as a production loss.

12.1.2 Assessing the risks

Risks to businesses by way of environmental accidents or disasters can be categorised as follows:

Table 12.1 Risks associated with main categories

Risk activity	Business	Design and installation	Operation and maintenance	Disposal
Health and safety	*	*	*	*
Hazardous substances		*	*	*
Fire and flood, external	*	*	*	*
Fire and flood, internal	*	*	*	*
Security	*	*	*	
Major disaster, e.g. air crash	*			
Interruption of utilities, e.g. electricity	*	*	*	
Performance brief	*	*		
Specification and design		*		
Configuration of plant and services		*		
Location of plant and services		*		
Access for installation and maintenance		*	*	
Maintainability		*	*	
Value engineering, value for money	*	*		
Delivery period	*	*		
Availability of spares	*	*	*	
Manufacturers' support	*	*	*	
Funding arrangements	*			
Form of contract	*	*		
Selection of installation contractors	*	*		
Installation programme	*	*		
Installation audit		*		
Testing and commissioning		*	*	
Health and safety file (CDM)		*	*	
Maintenance manual		*	*	
As-fitted drawings		*	*	
Records and plant history			*	
Post contract arrangements		*	*	
Maintenance programme			*	
Maintenance staff selection and training	*		*	
Permit-to-work			*	
Performance and quality audit		*	*	
Bench marking	*		*	

— external: flood, fire, breach of security and destruction of facilities, e.g. an air crash could interrupt externally provided services and utilities

— internal: flood, fire and interruption of services through inadequate design or installation.

The design (including the location of plant and equipment), installation, security, operation and continuing maintenance of the building service should be subjected to a risk assessment based on the requirements of the business. This assessment should take into account both external and internal risks and is best carried out by the client or prospective building user with guidance from the building services designer.

12.1.3 Performance brief and outline specification

The client's performance brief can be developed from the risk assessment and environmental requirements. It states the limits within which the building services will be expected to operate. The brief will take into account both external and internal risks and the operating and maintenance regime necessary for the installation to continue to operate within the stated limits.

It may be necessary for this brief to be presented in two parts — i.e. design/installation and operation/maintenance — depending on the procurement route. The performance brief may also require a value engineering assessment as part of the design. The outline specification will include the performance brief and recommendations on proven plant configurations or limitations known to apply to the design in hand.

12.1.4 Procurement, delivery and service options

Procurement risks include those associated with the specification, delivery, installation, testing and commissioning, and subsequent operation and maintenance of the plant. They also include contractual risks, especially where a number of subcontractors are involved.

The specified manufacturer must be able to support the maintenance of the plant with the provision of a range of spares, ideally for the full life of the installation. Delivery must be to an agreed installation programme within the relevant construction milestones. The installation must fit in with the way the plant has been designed, taking into account access and location problems and including ease of access for maintenance.

Risk activity	*Likelihood*				*Impact*			
	Negligible	*Low*	*Medium*	*High*	*Negligible*	*Low*	*Medium*	*High*
Business								
External factors (fire security, utilities)								
Internal factors (flood, inadequate design)								
Health and safety								
Major disaster								
Utility supply disruption								
Spares availability								
Design and installation								
Health and safety								
Satisfactory brief								
Specification								
Design								
Access								
Life expectancy								
Cost constraints								
Insurance								
Plant configuration								
Location of plant								
Delivery								
Installation programme								
Testing and commissioning								
Operation and maintenance								
Training								
Plant familiarisation								
Warranties								
Defects liability period								
Data storage and updating								
Statutory requirements								
Asset value								
Internal working environment								
Plant breakdown								
Maintenance personnel								
Permits to work								
Health and safety								
Hazardous materials								
Flood								
Fire								
Security								

Figure 12.1 Outline risk assessment format

Risk activity	*Likelihood*				*Impact*			
	Negligible	*Low*	*Medium*	*High*	*Negligible*	*Low*	*Medium*	*High*
Operation and maintenance cont'd								
Utility supply failure								
Access								
Maintainability								
Spares availability								
Maintenance manual								
Disposal								
Hazardous materials								
Fire								
Flood								
Security								
Health and safety								
Access								
Manufacturers' information								
Drawings								
Plant history								
Permit to work								

Figure 12.1 Outline risk assessment format — *continued*

Likelihood				
High	**	***	***	****
Medium	*	**	**	****
Low	*	*	**	***
Negligible	*	*	*	**
Impact	Negligible	Low	Medium	High

Key for action	
****	Top priority
***	Important
**	Low priority
*	Track and monitor

Figure 12.2 Chart to identify risk assessment results

Testing and commissioning may be given inadequate consideration at the design stage and the proper implementation of procedures is often adversely affected by programme pressures, sometimes to a serious degree. With installations that are technically complex, or where the design intent has not been clearly described, it is common for the systems not to be operating properly at handover. This may be for a variety of reasons, perhaps the most common being lack of commissioning time. Most installations, although made up of proven components, are bespoke and therefore need a settling-in period with close monitoring and adjustments so that components can be fine tuned. The remainder of the facility may not be fully functional, resulting in the plant not being used at design capacity. Seasonal adjustments may also need to be made and this is normally a specified requirement.

A defects liability period, typically of 12 months' duration, is normally included in a construction contract. This is to allow a reasonable period for the running-in of the building and plant and to allow time for any latent shortcomings to become apparent. The client needs to be given a clear understanding of its responsibilities during this period. Although the contractor remains responsible for the replacement of any faulty components or for remedial action on faulty workmanship, the client has to undertake sole responsibility for maintenance (see section 10).

One way to prevent confusion in this respect is to ensure that the routine maintenance (but not necessarily the operation) during the defects liability period is included as part of the installation contract. This ensures that only one agency, usually the installation contractor, is responsible for both maintenance and defects during this critical period.

The eventual owner of the installation must be able to operate and maintain it. Specialist contractors can be asked to do this or there may be an in-house capability. Often a mixture of the two is appropriate to obtain the range of skills necessary to meet all the requirements and to satisfy the risks. In all cases staff responsible for operating and maintaining the installation should undergo a period of familiarisation and training. A maintenance programme needs to be developed from the plant information sheets and operation and maintenance manuals if this has not already been included in the documentation provided under the contract. This is an area which can lead to unacceptable risks if it is overlooked or not properly resourced.

Contractual arrangements can greatly influence risk. The long contractual chain that includes many subcontractors is particularly vulnerable because it distances the manufacturers and installers from the client. One alternative is the appointment of a managing contractor in place of the main contractor, with all the subcontractors employed directly by the client. This produces a much 'flatter' structure: it gives the suppliers a clear picture of what the client wants and enables them to work together to achieve this.

Private finance initiatives (PFIs) (see section 4.2) seek to allocate risks for design, funding, installation and operation to those best able to manage them, leaving the service user to get on with its business while service providers get on with theirs.

12.2 Design and installation risks

12.2.1 Health and safety regulations

The design should be based on the performance brief developed from the assessment of the business requirements. The brief considers installation, operation, maintenance and *The Construction (Design and Management) Regulations*[1] (CDM Regulations) (see section 18 for further guidance). The client will need to have appointed a planning supervisor who has overall responsibility for coordinating the health and safety aspects of the design and planning phase, for the early stages of the health and safety plan and for the Health and Safety File. A designer has a duty under The CDM Regulations to avoid or minimise risks in construction and maintenance (see section 18). Design includes the preparation of specifications; it is not limited to drawings.

Typically, decisions will be reached on ease of access for maintenance and servicing, the provision of lifting arrangements for replacing components and safe procedures for the handling of oil and collection of refrigerants.

The principal contractor will need sufficient information from the planning stage health and safety plan to prepare suitable tenders and organise its own health and safety plan for the construction stage.

12.2.2 Design standards

The designer will need to confirm or comply with agreed standards. For example, the design may need to take account of particular standards required by the client in addition to basic British Standards and CIBSE recommendations. Life cycle cost considerations should also influence the design as much as initial costs and will certainly affect operational risk.

12.2.3 Insurance implications

The designer will need to research fully the insurance requirements and include these in the design and specification. This is of particular importance where an existing installation is extended or included as part of a new installation. A requirement to design an extension for an installation to a tight specification may, for example, mean that closer tolerances need to be taken into account.

12.2.4 Reducing operational risks at the design stage

The level of business risk will determine the amount of investment required to design and install back-up or duplicate systems for the building services. Out of this will come the decision to provide standby plant and whether an automatic changeover is necessary.

Duplication of systems will introduce the requirement to assess common node failure points. For example, an acceptable common node failure point on an electrical system may be at the final connection to a bus-bar, which has inherently high reliability, but not at a changeover switch, which could suffer mechanical failure. This will lead to a discussion as to whether separate interlocked changeover switches are required, giving break before make. If the reverse — i.e. make before break — is required an uninterruptible power supply (UPS) could be considered and, depending on the configuration and reliability of the public power supply, standby generation.

The necessity for, and level of, monitoring and control by a building energy management system (BEMS) will be agreed. All alarms may be important, but only some will be of the highest priority and therefore in need of more than routine attention. Again these critical alarms may be further reduced by specifying modular plant (e.g. boilers, water chillers) so that the failure of a single unit will not reduce the plant output below the required level; this would minimise out-of-hours attendance.

12.3 Operation and maintenance risks

Building managers will be well aware of the teething problems associated with the handover of new installations and the risks involved. Ideally the handover should be preceded by a thorough training and familiarisation period for those who are to be responsible for the ongoing operation and maintenance. An ideal time is during final installation and commissioning.

Warranty and defects liability arrangements also need to be spelt out. On large installations, maintenance during the defects liability period should ideally be included as part of the contract for the installation contractor. This avoids any misunderstanding over responsibility for failure of components.

Provision for storing and updating of information on the installation needs resourcing. Record drawings, commissioning data, test sheets, and operation and maintenance information can soon be destroyed or lost if data control systems are not provided. Without this information it is almost impossible to maintain and/or recalibrate the installation to its original design standard.

12.3.1 Maintenance programme

A maintenance programme is required to:

— meet health and safety and statutory requirements

— protect the assets of the installation and building

— continue to provide the specified service/working environment.

The maintenance programme will need to be developed from an assessment of statutory requirements, manufacturers' recommendations and operational risk. To overmaintain is expensive; to undermaintain is not cost effective as it leads to a deterioration of plant and service.

12.3.2 Maintenance arrangements

Maintenance arrangements may be loosely categorised as:

— breakdown or reactive: maintenance is carried out only when the plant has broken down (may be under a form of call-out only contract as outlined in section 4.3.9)

— planned or planned preventive maintenance (PPM): maintenance according to a predetermined time schedule based on historical operating data (see section 4.3.4 for typical contract arrangement)

— condition-based: the condition of the plant is monitored continuously, or at regular intervals, and the maintenance routines and frequencies adjusted to respond to any changes in the agreed parameters of plant output or condition.

A good maintenance programme in a complex building will integrate all these categories of maintenance to provide cost-effective maintenance within the health and safety, statutory, asset protection and operational risk requirements. See also section 3.

12.3.3 Maintenance staff

Underskilled staff can cause enormous damage to plant and equipment and represent a very high level of risk. Staff must be carefully selected for their knowledge and ability in relation to the complexity of the installation. A system of staff evaluation, motivation and training is part of any good maintenance programme.

12.3.4 Areas of high risk

Installations such as high voltage or steam systems require special operating and maintenance skills, procedures and training, with the use of highly managed permit-to-work and access requirements. Method statements or written procedures will be required for less critical situations. Evaporative cooling towers are particularly associated with the risk of Legionnaires' disease, which can be controlled only within the framework of a formal and properly managed and audited programme of operation and maintenance.

12.3.5 Audit requirements

Plant performance and maintenance standards and procedures should be audited continuously or at regular intervals against the maintenance programme, plant output and staff or contractor performance. A system of bench marking should also be established. Graphic records are useful for clearly indicating trends in plant operation and performance.

12.4 Disposal risks

A time will come with any installation when it needs to be disposed of or replaced. The plant should not represent a higher risk at this time than when it is in use. Regulations now exist for the control of hazardous substances such as asbestos and refrigerant gases. The CDM Regulations[(1)] include those for 'the removal of a structure or part of a structure or of any product of waste resulting from demolition or dismantling of a structure or from dissembly of prefabricated elements which, immediately before dissembly, formed a structure'.

Removing plant and equipment from occupied areas presents its own special risks, especially if operational status (e.g. a production process) is to be maintained. Work needs to be carefully planned and coordinated to contain the risks. At such times other risks — for example, from fire and flooding — are increased and additional precautions and adequate contingency plans should be in place.

Complications can arise where later additions to the original installation or building restrict access to the original installation, making it difficult to dismantle or maintain the plant. This can result in considerable cost above that required for the main task.

References

1 *The Construction, Design and Management Regulations 1994* Statutory Instrument 1994 No. 3140 (London: Stationery Office) (1994)

Bibliography

Handover information for building services BSRIA Technical Note **TN15/95** (Bracknell: Building Services Research and Information Association) (1995)

13 Owning and operating costs

Contents

Summary

Cost data are broken down under four headings: utilities, consumables and spares, specialist services and labour. The use of bench marking and targeting techniques to assess actual cost elements is discussed.

The presentation of information on three levels is proposed: first, details of the building or premises; secondly, an asset list of fittings and plant; and, thirdly, maintenance routines and procedures and planned and unplanned work. Detailed descriptions are offered for each level.

In a similar way, labour utilisation is split into 20 typical duties: 10 planned and 10 unplanned activities.

Some of the factors to be taken into account when investigating costs for new buildings and designs are outlined and simple accounting techniques dealt with.

Two investment appraisal techniques are described in detail: simple payback and net present value. Simple example calculations of the latter are shown together with tables of discount factors.

Some coverage of life cycle costing is also provided.

This section provides important information on the financial aspects of owning and operating building services installations and is relevant to both designers and building operators. It includes information on cost data and its uses in managing building services and also covers practical aspects of bench marking, basic accountancy and cost predictions associated with refurbishment or new construction.

13.1 Cost data

Reasons for the collection of cost data are twofold: first, to ensure that payments claimed by suppliers or contractors are fair and reasonable and, secondly, to help in planning and budgeting the building's expenditure. Care should be taken to ensure that the cost of collecting and logging data does not outweigh its usefulness.

There are four main types of cost data: utilities, consumables and spares, specialist services and labour.

13.1.1. Utilities

The simplest forms of cost data to collect are those that appear in invoices which the building operator receives for goods or services. Of these, the simplest to collect are the data contained in utility invoices, e.g. for electricity, gas, fuel oil and water. All building operators should keep their own records of meter readings to ensure that the utility providers are invoicing correctly. Readings should be taken with, at the very least, the same frequency as the utility company bills, for example, monthly or quarterly. Care must be taken in evaluating the invoices due to the complexity of differing contract or tariff arrangements. Building operators should, therefore, have a thorough understanding of the utility supply contract, especially penalties payable for increased consumption.

Utility-use cost data are relatively simple to analyse against a number of performance indicators or targets. This is due in part to the formalised presentation of the information with little variation between companies.

13.1.2 Materials, spares and consumables

The next type of cost data is associated with invoicing for the supply of materials, consumables, spare parts and replacement equipment. This form of cost data is an important component of the operating costs of a building and must be clearly identifiable if performance indicators are to be produced and to ensure financial probity in the ordering of and paying for goods.

Each invoice should be clearly identifiable with an order. Unfortunately, the need for spares is often urgent — for example in emergency maintenance — and the paperwork associated with a verbal order is not always completed. The presentation of information on invoices also often follows no particular form. Building owners should therefore develop their own records associated with such costs. These records could be incorporated as a database or spreadsheet related to a particular period, for example, monthly or quarterly. A minimum series of data is listed below:

(*a*) name of supplier

(*b*) order number

(*c*) date of order

(*d*) quoted/estimated cost

(*e*) date of supply

(*f*) invoice number

(*g*) invoiced amount

(*h*) amount of any variation and reason(s).

To simplify the comparison of cost trends, the building owner should endeavour to place replacement orders for particular items on a regular basis.

13.1.3 Specialist services

Cost data associated with specialist services — for example, water treatment companies supplying materials, specialist labour and water quality analyses — are more complex. In these cases the costs can be a mixture of fixed and variable costs, changing with each visit to the building. Even more care is needed in collecting and checking such data.

A minimum series of data is:

(*a*) name of specialist

(*b*) date of site visit

(*c*) estimated cost (based on original contract)

(*d*) estimate of materials/spares used in visit

(*e*) invoice number, date and value

(*f*) comments.

In some cases the provision of specialist services is based on a 'fixed contract value' and it may be treated as any other material.

13.1.4 Maintenance and operation labour

This type of cost data can be for either directly employed labour or labour provided by a contractor. In the case of the contractor, it is relatively simple to collect cost data in terms of an hourly, daily or other time-based rate, differing rates applying for different trades and skill levels. The same approach should be taken as with materials in that invoices for labour supplied must be checked against what was actually provided. This can be the source of much dispute, especially in the provision of 'call-out' response where there may be additional charges associated with responses to an emergency situation.

With directly employed labour, it is often difficult to obtain accurate cost data as details of an individual's wages or salary details are considered confidential and are not dealt with by the maintenance and operations management. At the very least, the hours worked by each grade of staff must be collected to allow planning and control. Ideally, for each trade and skill level an inclusive rate should be determined which incorporates the full cost of employment including all overheads. For example, this may include National Insurance and pension contributions, allowances for cover for holiday, sickness and training (either by overtime by others or temporary staff), the cost of staff facilities, an allowance for personnel management, safety management, any other support function they make use of and any additional corporate benefits such as subsidised travel.

13.2 Bench marking

The object of bench marking is to be able to compare any particular activity with other samples from a peer group to determine whether performance is above or below a selected datum level. It is important to differentiate whether the peer group used in the bench mark is a simple average, best practice or an acceptable minimum.

One of the major disadvantages with bench marks is the difficulty in ensuring that the comparison being drawn is truly equitable. In the case of a single organisation making comparisons based upon internally generated data this should be simple to achieve. Where a broad, general bench mark is used, extreme care needs to be taken to ensure that the correct data are used.

With regard to the range of activities associated with producing a working environment, the British Institute of Facilities Management (BIFM) has produced a *Facilities management measurement protocol*(1). This provides brief details on which data to collect in order to carry out measurement of the facilities management operation in a building. It defines a variety of cost centres, some of which are concerned with building services. The chief ones are:

(*a*) utilities costs (as a subheading under services charge/overheads)

(*b*) air-conditioning costs (as a subheading of internal moves)

(*c*) maintenance costs, subdivided into:

— building fabric

— fixtures and fittings

— mechanical services

— electrical services

— lifts

— fire systems

— cyclic redecorations

— environmental monitoring.

It is important that equipment upgrades, refurbishment and the maintenance of production and process equipment and systems are excluded from such cost centres as these are not germane to facilities management activities and in many instances may be considered as exceptional costs.

The BIFM protocol further recommends that at least five samples are required for internal comparison and, for external comparisons, a minimum of 20 data sets.

13.3 Cost data attributes

When analysing building services maintenance costs in detail, the data should have certain attributes:

— easy and cheap to collect and manipulate

— reliable, i.e. difficult to make mistakes in recording, calculating and presenting

— compatible with overall organisation objectives

— early indicators of poor performance and likely consequences

— known limitations to their use

— suitable for analysis to provide indication of remedial measures required.

13.4 Levels of information

In being able to plan and control expenditure, operation and maintenance information can be considered to exist on three levels.

13.4.1 Global maintenance

The uppermost level of information is that concerned with the building characteristics — for example, size, use and occupancy — and the overall totals of maintenance and operational expenditure. The collection of these may be used to provide useful bench marks for comparisons with, for example, other buildings or maintenance contractors. They will also allow cost analyses to be carried out and highlight any deficiencies in the planned maintenance regime or in the energy efficiency of the operation. Collection of much of the data will be a one-off exercise or, where they vary annually, available within an organisation's accounting systems.

Based on BSRIA Technical Memoranda TM3/91 *Maintenance and utility costs: results of a survey*[2], information should be collected on the following major details of the building or premises:

(*a*) postal address

(*b*) site exposure

(*c*) orientation of building

(*d*) aspect ratio and number of floors of building

(*e*) type and use of building

(*f*) type of construction

(*g*) age of building

(*h*) age of building services

(*i*) floor area of building (whatever factor is used in assessing the value of the building, i.e. nett lettable area or gross floor area)

(*j*) building population, type(s) and number

(*k*) building occupation pattern(s)

(*l*) building services system types

— heating and hot water service system

— air conditioning system(s) if applicable

— electrical distribution system

— lift installations, type and number

— utility supply details

— public health systems

(*m*) number of staff engaged in maintenance work, trades and levels/grades

(*n*) contract maintenance arrangements: level of risk assigned to contractor by contractual conditions and value

(*o*) maintenance policy pursued: this may differ between systems (see section 3)

(*p*) annual maintenance cost totals (note that the subtotal of planned and unplanned work should equal the subtotal of labour, materials and contract costs) for:

— planned maintenance

— unplanned maintenance

— labour

— materials

— contract

(*q*) utility cost totals (total consumption and any sub-metering):

— electricity: total costs including standing charges, units consumed, cost per unit, maximum demand, connection charge etc.

— gas: as for electricity where applicable

— oil: as for electricity where applicable

— other fuels: as for electricity where applicable

— water: consumption and disposal costs.

The division between planned and unplanned maintenance and the division between utilities used to produce the environment and that used in process consumption is very important but may be difficult to segregate.

One of the most influential factors on maintenance costs is the level of service required by the building occupier, which is difficult to identify objectively. The level of service depends primarily on the type of maintenance response to a contingency and the speed with which this is made. These factors, in turn, can be influenced by the organisation of the occupier and its managerial policy with respect to the service personnel. Many building services maintenance organisations perform functions, such as small works, in addition to specific maintenance tasks.

13.4.2 Systems and assets

The second level of information concerns the characteristics of the systems and plant items. The collection of these data is normally a one-off exercise and will lead to an essential understanding of the relative importance of items of plant and the building function which, in turn, should be used to determine appropriate maintenance policies.

The information should consist of a list of the building services systems installed, ranked in accordance to the relationship between the system and the building function — for example, the electrical distribution system may be considered to be the most crucial to the building function and would, therefore, have the highest ranking.

A sublist of plant items within a building services system is often referred to as an asset list and is essential when considering maintenance approaches to individual items. It should contain information about each item used within each system and upon which maintenance, planned or unplanned, may be carried out. Ductwork, pipework, electrical distribution etc. can also be considered as plant items.

Care must be taken not to create too large a database of information by considering individual items to a very detailed level. At the initial stage it is unlikely that a building would be considered to have more than 100 types of plant item: it may have multiples of certain items, such as room terminal devices, but is not always necessary to identify these individually.

This asset list should detail:

(*a*) the plant item function

(*b*) the geographical location within the building

(*c*) the manufacturer's/supplier's name and address

(*d*) model description/type

(*e*) model number

(*f*) rating or capacity

(*g*) number installed

(*h*) cost of purchase

(*i*) cost of installation

(*j*) date of installation

(*k*) factor used in any capitalisation scheme

(*l*) factor relating the plant item's importance in relation to the system/building function.

This information is the backbone to creating a planned maintenance system and may be developed to whatever level of detail suits organisational needs. It can form the basis of building a service history and will be of use in valuing a building throughout its life and in ensuring that information concerning the building services is accessible to the whole of the occupying organisation and not in the sole possession of a few individuals. The list of items of plant and their relationship with the building function would also be helpful to the facilities manager when discussing forward planning and costings with non-engineering personnel and could also be used in contract negotiations with, for example, maintenance contractors to set priorities.

13.4.3 Maintenance tasks

The third level of information deals with the actual maintenance work that is carried out on individual systems and items of plant (the information for the asset list must exist before that for maintenance is compiled). Collection of this can produce considerable quantities of data and careful thought must be given to the value of the information produced and the uses it may be put to compared with the cost of collecting, collating and presenting it.

The information to be collected relates to planned and unplanned maintenance work. It is considered unlikely that any one item of equipment will have more than 10 individual maintenance work 'packages' carried out in any one year and that unplanned or breakdown work may be related to one or more causes.

For the majority of maintenance work much of the cost is labour related and it is therefore necessary to know the employment costs of that labour. Where actual employment data are not available, a nominal hourly rate for each labour grade which works with that item of equipment must be used if the efficacy of that equipment is to be assessed in terms of reliability, cost to maintain, value to an organisation etc.

For each maintenance task, planned or unplanned, the minimum level of detail would be:

(*a*) item of plant being worked upon

(*b*) job/maintenance procedure applied

(*c*) time taken

(*d*) grade of operative(s)

(*e*) cost of materials.

The amount of information that would be produced at this level can be considerable and the use of a computer database is recommended.

It is important to be able to differentiate between planned and unplanned expenditure: in many cases, unplanned expenditure exceeds that which is planned.

The planned maintenance can be considered in relation to the frequency at which each task is carried out and will be predominantly based on regular (for example, yearly, quarterly, monthly, weekly) inspection, cleaning and replacement of consumables and irregular tasks associated with remedial work, replacement or redundancy. Care must be taken in selecting general job titles to allow later manipulation of the data. A range of titles could be:

— inspection
— cleaning
— safety checks
— testing
— calibration
— replacement of consumables
— replacement of parts
— refurbishment of plant
— replacement of plant.

Note that fault finding/diagnosis is a combination of inspection and testing.

Unplanned work can be considered in relation to the cause. Again general titles should be used and a typical short list might be:

— wear/corrosion/other progressive deterioration
— manufacturing defect
— material defect

- design defect
- installation defect
- inadequate maintenance
- maintenance reassembly defect
- maintenance adjustment defect
- operational mistake
- malicious damage.

If information is collected at this level, the total cost of the individual maintenance items should equal the total expenditure and could be a useful corroboration between budget costings and actual expenditure. Correctly manipulated, the database will rapidly identify poor workmanship (i.e. repeated breakdowns), unreliable plant, plant that is costly to maintain, specific deficiencies in the regular planned work and many other useful items of maintenance management information. Most importantly it will allow improved accuracy of forward planning and realistic maintenance budgets to be set and justified.

13.5 Utilisation of labour

The following provides a systematic approach to identifying core activities of maintenance operatives so that comparisons may be drawn between buildings, contractors or even individual technicians or craftsmen. Careful analysis of such labour utilisation will also produce indicators of the effectiveness of maintenance management and the actual work carried out. It is important to be able to distinguish between planned and unplanned expenditure: in many cases, unplanned expenditure can equal or even exceed the planned expenditure.

Each of the main work categories are broken into 10 sub-headings, including one for 'other' work. If this catch-all heading occupies significant operative time to keep the plant in working order, an in-depth investigation of the maintenance system is warranted as the other headings typify most of the maintenance activities.

13.5.1 Planned activities

These including the following:

(*a*) replenishment/replacement of consumables

(*b*) inspection

(*c*) functional testing

(*d*) electrical safety testing

(*e*) repairs, resulting from (*b*) to (*d*)

(*f*) supervision/receiving particular instructions

(*g*) procurement of materials, tools, spares and equipment

(*h*) travelling, cleaning and tidying

(*i*) minor new or improvement work initiated by maintenance management

(*j*) other planned activities (including training).

13.5.2 Unplanned activities

These include:

(*a*) response to complaints to assess situation

(*b*) remedial work which results from (*a*)

(*c*) attendance to unforeseen failure including fault diagnosis

(*d*) emergency repairs associated with (*c*)

(*e*) minor new or improvement works initiated outside maintenance organisation

(*f*) major new works (not strictly maintenance activities but often involve maintenance operatives directly or indirectly)

(*g*) dedicated travelling time (this is often significant in unplanned work)

(*h*) tidying and cleaning following contingency and/or unplanned work.

(*i*) materials, tools and equipment procurement (often involves significant time to identify precise requirement)

(*j*) other unplanned activities (includes attendance time for other trades, visitors etc.).

13.6 Backlog of maintenance

It is an unfortunate fact that planned maintenance (and hence expenditure) must often be deferred or even dropped as a result of expenditure cuts to meet overall operating cost limits. Many non-engineering management personnel view maintenance activities as an optional luxury that produces no tangible benefit. It is important to record not only the work dropped (and the reasons for this) but the consequential results of not doing the work. With the increasing emphasis on health and safety legislation, this information may be needed in any court proceedings arising from an accident that occurs as a result of maintenance deferred or not carried out.

Conversely, unnecessary maintenance activities should be identified from the use of bench marks or other means of comparative assessment and maintenance programmes suitably adjusted to redeploy or reduce resources.

13.7 Data priorities

Owning and operating cost estimates are, typically, generated by the design team with the major inputs from the system designer while the main user of the data is the system operator. Each party has differing priorities.

For the designer, the ability to produce accurate predictions of the capital and life cycle costs are paramount so that the engineering design decisions have the backing of financial justification. In the past, the new works sector has been concerned principally with first costs; the designer's major priority has therefore been the estimation of the capital cost of major items of plant — the cost of materials and installation. As a result of both private finance initiative (PFI) projects (see section 4.3.12) and the need to improve energy efficiency, it is increasingly important for the designer to be able to estimate accurately energy use and other operating costs. The use of modern thermal modelling software should facilitate energy consumption costing and improve its accuracy. Estimating the maintenance costs is far more difficult as there are no wide-coverage databases of information publicly available to allow comparisons; section 13.8 gives details of some areas to be considered.

For the building operator the priorities are different. First, the data collected should be able to demonstrate financial probity and, secondly, it should enable the operator to evaluate whether value for money is being achieved. This is the balance between the effectiveness of the maintenance in support of the business function of the building and the acceptability of the costs. This will involve collecting data that will permit the examination of trends in expenditure while facilitating historical comparisons and highlighting performance indicators.

13.8 Cost predictions for new buildings and designs

Cost predictions for engineering services in the course of design have to be based on historical data derived from similar installations or components and need to take into account various factors that will be specific to the proposed scheme. Some of these factors will be difficult to express in financial terms.

These influencing factors, in addition to the obvious ones of building footprint, major plant items, and rule-of-thumb installation costs, include:

— Quality of the environment required: this is a complex measure taking into account the air tightness of the building envelope, type and size of fenestration, and the degree of control required for temperature and humidity.

— Budget limits and constraints set by the client: at this stage of the prediction it is important to understand fully the client's financial status given that almost all projects overrun their original budgets. It is tempting to use broadbrush unit floor costs but these should be used only as very broad guides.

— Systems suggested: this involves understanding the client's need for the building and what is acceptable in terms of floor and ceiling space devoted to building services. In addition to likely capital and installation costs, it will be necessary to know the relative merits and limits of each system in terms of its likely energy effectiveness (and hence energy consumption) and maintenance costs (routine repetitive replacement of consumables, such as filters, together with an allowance for a number of breakdowns and replacement of subassemblies).

— Weather conditions specific to the site: this will affect the quality of plant exposed on rooftops etc., the need for frost protection and likely energy consumption.

— Occupant type and their expectations: this relates to the quality of environment to be achieved and the required response of the maintenance personnel to occupant complaints.

— Occupancy patterns: these can affect both energy consumption and the costs of maintenance in terms of when plant can be taken out of service for carrying out maintenance. Changes to the planned intervals between inspections may be necessary to account for increased running hours if occupancy hours are extended and an 'hours run' maintenance policy is applied.

— Maintenance policy to be applied: whether a 'do nothing', a time-based or condition-based policy is to be operated. This cost will also be influenced by the degree of reliability required from the systems and plant, which clients often do not define. (Note that a building owner operating a 'do nothing' maintenance policy could be open to action from the Health and Safety Executive in the event of an accident resulting from the absence of inspections or servicing.)

— Specialist requirements of the plant for maintenance: whether, for example, water treatment costs or building management system maintenance need to be taken into consideration.

— Geographical location: this is especially important in terms of availability of local labour (for installation and maintenance) and transport logistics.

Once the scheme design is finished, more detailed maintenance cost estimates may be built up based on the knowledge of the engineering services and plant to be installed. Much of this is concerned with:

— numbers and capacities of the principal items of plant, e.g. heat generators, chillers, calorifiers, controls and pumps

— extent and complexity of control system

— extent of distributed plant and equipment, e.g. number of room terminal units, total length of pipe and ductwork systems

There are a various sources of data for carrying out rule-of-thumb cost calculations, including:

(*a*) Building Cost Information Service (BCIS), 12 Great George Street, Parliament Square, London, SW1P 3AD

(*b*) *Spon's mechanical and electrical services price book*(3)

(*c*) Published examples: cost models have been published in the *Building Services Journal* as follows:

— commercial offices (urban environment)(4)

— commercial offices (non-urban environment)(5)

— shopping centres(6)

— IT cabling(7)

— theatres(8)

— schools(9)

— swimming pools(10)

— combined heat and power (CHP)(11)

- private hospitals[12]
- commercial restaurants (provincial city centres)[13]
- art galleries and museums[14]
- lifts and escalators[15]
- building energy management systems[16]
- kitchens and serveries[17]

(*d*) Specialist cost consultants.

13.9 Simple accounting techniques

Double entry book-keeping is a system that reports what profit the business has made, how much the business owes and how much is owed to the business.

Modern accounting falls broadly into two categories:

- financial accounting, which is concerned with the supply of information to an owner as to how well the business is doing
- management accounting, which is concerned with the supply of information to a manager for use in planning and in controlling the business

The task of dealing with owning and operating costs is largely one of management accounting, particularly with regard to ensuring that the building's services are effective in achieving the right internal environment for the occupying business and is doing so efficiently. The two main branches of management accounting relevant to owning and operating costs are budgetary control and capital investment appraisal.

13.9.1 Budgetary control

Before control can be exercised, a budget must be drawn up. The Chartered Institute of Management Accountants (CIMA) defines a budget as: 'A plan expressed in money. It is prepared and approved prior to the budget period and may show income, expenditure and the capital to be employed.'

A maintenance budget should be drawn up as 'zero-based' — that is, working from basic principles and not just incrementing the previous period's figures. This encourages the independent assessment of each activity followed by a suitable combination of the whole range of activities to match available funds. In reality, for an existing building some cognisance of historical financial performance will be taken but must be tempered by what needs to be done in the future together with a careful assessment of the scope for improvement.

The essential features of a maintenance budget are as follows:

- It lays down policies that should be followed to ensure that the overall maintenance objectives are achieved. This means operating and maintaining the plant in such a way and with such staff as are necessary to achieve an acceptable level of availability. It includes the funding and planned replacement of plant that can no longer be economically repaired, is obsolete, is too inefficient or is rendered redundant due to legislative or other action, e.g. phasing out ozone-depleting refrigerants such as CFCs or HCFCs.
- It contains quantitative and financial data, which are formally documented.
- It covers a defined future period of time.

Once the budget exists, it may be used for control purposes. Budgetary control may be summarised as:

- clearly defining the financial responsibilities of the relevant management
- detailing a plan of action within the manager's sphere of responsibility; this may be in terms of labour, materials and new equipment
- ensuring the manager adheres to the budget
- monitoring the performance and comparing the results at relevant intervals with the budgeted figures
- considering, recommending and approving corrective action if actual results differ
- investigating any such variances that are unaccounted for
- permitting deliberate departures from the budget only if approved by senior management.

In building services terms, the budget for owning, operating and maintaining is likely to be only one part of a master budget for a business. The nature of building use can change or failures may occur which cannot be accurately forecast when the budget is compiled. Budgets for operating buildings, therefore, must have a degree of flexibility to cope with such changes. This may be identified as a contingency sum or the nature of the organisation may be such that it can deal with changes to the budget during the budget period. In either case, such changes must be justified.

Table 13.1 provides a checklist for preparing a budget for maintenance.

13.9.2 Capital investment appraisal

In undertaking a capital investment appraisal it is important to understand the difference between capital and revenue expenditure. Capital expenditure is defined as the cost of acquiring, producing or enhancing fixed assets. Revenue expenditure is defined as expenditure on the supply and manufacture of goods and the provision of services charged in the accounting period in which they are consumed. This includes repairs and depreciation of the fixed assets as distinct from the provision of those assets.

Generally, capital expenditure has some important characteristics that must be taken into account in the appraisal. For example, it is likely to include substantial expenditure, the benefits could be spread over many years, the benefits may be difficult to predict, it will have an impact on the organisation's employees and it will help the organisation achieve its objectives.

Table 13.1 Maintenance budget checklist

Category	Item
Labour	In-house trades: supervision, management and training
	Contract: mobile, resident, supplementary for labour-intensive tasks (e.g. tank and domestic water system chlorination, and checking of electrical connections)
	Specialist subcontractors: for specialist tasks (e.g. controls, lifts, uninterruptible power supplies and lifting equipment)
Materials	Replenishment (e.g. oils, greases and fuel oils)
	Replacement routine (e.g. filters and belts)
	Replacement non-routine (e.g. pipework, cables and lamps)
Equipment	Replacement of life-expired plant
	Replacement of plant that has suffered catastrophic failure
	Replacement of worn parts
	Repair of misuse and abuse damage
	Energy efficiency improvements (e.g. light fittings and controls)
	Enhancements in aid of maintenance efficiency improvements (e.g. condition monitoring modifications)
	Disposal of redundant plant
Specialist resources	Consultants for auditing and change management (e.g. planning system improvements, and energy and safety audits
	Specialist contractors (e.g. cooling tower maintenance, lift re-roping and water treatment)
Management	Planned maintenance system (e.g labour to implement and operate hardware and software consumables such as disks, tapes and paper)
	Legal compliance (e.g. documentation)
	Insurance
	Training
Diagnostics	Development of feedback mechanisms, condition monitoring, one-off investigations (e.g. failure of complex plant)
	Environment
	Air quality surveys, disposal of cleaning and water treatment chemicals
Utilities	Electricity consumption and connection charges (contract re-negotiation): lighting, small power, HVAC, lifts/transportation, catering
	Gas: heating, catering and hot water production
	Water: supply, sewerage, fire, treatment, rebate for evaporative use (e.g. cooling towers)

However, not all aspects of these definitions are applicable to owning and operating buildings. Capital expenditure will typically be for replacing worn-out or obsolete plant or for the partial or complete replacement of systems to enhance the environmental control within the building or improve energy efficiency (for example, investment in CHP plant). It may also include the removal of redundant plant that will have some second-hand or substantial scrap value.

In the case of manufacturing industry, the benefit from capital investment is often easy to quantify in, say, increased output or reduced production costs, both of which affect the outcome of the appraisal. When it comes to capital investment in building services, however, there are often no tangible benefits in terms of increased profitability. The benefit from installing air conditioning in a heated-only building will be increased occupant comfort and, possibly, increased productivity; against this there is likely to be increased energy consumption and increased maintenance requirements. The advantages are impossible to evaluate financially, while the disadvantages are very easy to cost. Capital appraisal is most influenced by items that have an accurate monetary value.

There are five basic techniques for capital appraisal:

- payback
- discounted payback
- accounting rate of return
- net present value
- internal rate of return.

Of these, only two — payback and net present value — have direct relevance to owning and operating costs.

13.9.2.1 Payback

This is a very simple technique of deciding how long it will take for net profit on a project to pay off the original investment. It can be rapidly calculated to assess and compare a number of projects and will indicate how long each option will take to recoup the investment. For use in the context of operating buildings, there has to be some tangible return from the project such as a reduction in energy consumption, a decrease in maintenance effort leading to labour and/or materials savings or a change of fuel leading to reduced fuel costs.

The technique consists of evaluating the net cashflow of the project, taking the original investment and reducing the total by the savings (minus any instalments paid on the amount borrowed) in each relevant period (say annually) until the net sum outstanding is reduced to zero. The time taken to offset the investment is expressed in years and is termed the 'payback period'.

The disadvantages of this technique is that it does not take account of:

- changing value of money with time (e.g. the effect of inflation)
- the stage in the payback period when the major proportion of the investment is recovered. A short payback period option may recover most of the investment in the latter stages and this may represent a risk
- the profit made once the payback is achieved — a project with the shortest payback period may be selected even though there may be other options with longer payback periods that, in the longer term, would be more profitable
- the actual amount of the original investment — a high-cost project with high future profitability may be rejected in favour of a lower-cost project with a short payback.

13.9.2.2 Net present value

This is accepted by financial concerns as the most appropriate method of capital investment appraisal as it can take into account the value of money over time, the profitability of a project and the return on the investment. It is important to understand that this technique produces only a figure to evaluate the financial desirability of a number of project options: there may be many other factors to take into account in the final selection other than purely cost.

The main disadvantage is that of selecting an appropriate rate of interest to apply as over time interest rates vary considerably in a way that is not predictable.

The technique consists of combining the original investment with each of the future costs and incomes associated with an option that will occur over a specific period of time and calculating their value in terms of a single point in time (using the same principles as involved in compound interest).

Discount factor tables

To enable future one-off payments or savings to be evaluated in terms of the single point in time, discount tables can be used to determine the value of money invested or discounted. Table 13.2 contains a series of discount factors derived from the formula:

$$f = 1 / (1 + I)^n$$

where f is the discount factor, I is the interest or inflation rate (expressed as a decimal) and n is the number of years.

In practical terms, the discount factors may be used to determine the single sum of money that must be invested now to yield a specific value at a certain point in the future assuming a constant rate of interest.

Example: a payment of £100 is due in 10 years' time and the assumed inflation rate is 10%; what is the present or equivalent value of money?

$$100 \times [1 / (1 + 0.1)^{10}] = £38.55$$

Cumulative discount factors

An alternative view might be what sum of money must be invested to yield £100 in 10 years' time, assuming an interest rate of 10% per annum? If the payment is repeated and constant, a similar factor can be calculated to determine the present value of all such payments. Table 13.3 gives a series of cumulative discount factors derived from the formula:

$$c = \{1 - [(1 + I)^{-n}]\} / I$$

where c is the cumulative factor, I is the interest or inflation rate (expressed as a decimal) and n is the number of years over which an annual payment will be made.

Cumulative discount factors may be used to determine a single value today representing regular payments for a fixed time at a fixed interest rate. For example, a single value today can be calculated for the payments for planned maintenance visits over the life of the plant or the purchase of regular consumables such as disposable air filters.

Example: an annual payment of £10 is made for 10 years at a constant inflation rate of 10%; what is the present value of all those payments?

$$10 \times \{1 - [(1 + 0.1)^{-10}]\} / 0.1 = £61.45$$

Each of the components of a project can be similarly adjusted to their net present value so that an overall value of the project can be determined and compared with, say, the benefit of investing the same sum of money elsewhere.

13.9.2.3 Investment appraisal

The three remaining techniques for the capital appraisal all have major disadvantages that invariably make them unsuitable for assessment of building services projects:

- Discounted payback: while it does take account of the value of money over time, it concentrates only on the cash recovery of the investment and ignores what happens after the payback period. The payback period using this technique is always longer than that for simple payback.
- Accounting rate of return: compares the profit made with the capital invested expressed as a percentage. This is inappropriate for most building services projects as very few make a clearly quantifiable profit.
- Internal rate of return: very similar to net present value but seeks to determine what rate of return would be required to ensure the total net present value equals the total initial cost. As income from building services projects often does not occur, this method is not appropriate.

Table 13.2 Discount factor table: present value of £1.00, received after n years, discounted at I%: $f = 1/(1+I)^n$

Year	Discount factor for stated annual interest rate (%)																			
	1	2	3	4	5	6	7	8	9	10	11	12	13	14	15	16	17	18	19	20
1	0.9901	0.9804	0.9709	0.9615	0.9524	0.9434	0.9346	0.9259	0.9174	0.9091	0.9009	0.8929	0.8850	0.8772	0.8696	0.8621	0.8547	0.8475	0.8403	0.8333
2	0.9803	0.9612	0.9426	0.9246	0.9070	0.8900	0.8734	0.8573	0.8417	0.8264	0.8116	0.7972	0.7831	0.7695	0.7561	0.7432	0.7305	0.7182	0.7062	0.6944
3	0.9706	0.9423	0.9151	0.8890	0.8638	0.8396	0.8163	0.7938	0.7722	0.7513	0.7312	0.7118	0.6931	0.6750	0.6575	0.6407	0.6244	0.6086	0.5934	0.5787
4	0.9610	0.9238	0.8885	0.8548	0.8227	0.7921	0.7629	0.7350	0.7084	0.6830	0.6587	0.6355	0.6133	0.5921	0.5718	0.5523	0.5337	0.5158	0.4987	0.4823
5	0.9515	0.9057	0.8626	0.8219	0.7835	0.7473	0.7130	0.6806	0.6499	0.6209	0.5935	0.5674	0.5428	0.5194	0.4972	0.4761	0.4561	0.4371	0.4190	0.4019
6	0.9420	0.8880	0.8375	0.7903	0.7462	0.7050	0.6663	0.6302	0.5963	0.5645	0.5346	0.5066	0.4803	0.4556	0.4323	0.4104	0.3898	0.3704	0.3521	0.3349
7	0.9327	0.8706	0.8131	0.7599	0.7107	0.6651	0.6227	0.5835	0.5470	0.5132	0.4817	0.4523	0.4251	0.3996	0.3759	0.3538	0.3332	0.3139	0.2959	0.2791
8	0.9235	0.8535	0.7894	0.7307	0.6768	0.6274	0.5820	0.5403	0.5019	0.4665	0.4339	0.4039	0.3762	0.3506	0.3269	0.3050	0.2848	0.2660	0.2487	0.2326
9	0.9143	0.8368	0.7664	0.7026	0.6446	0.5919	0.5439	0.5002	0.4604	0.4241	0.3909	0.3606	0.3329	0.3075	0.2843	0.2630	0.2434	0.2255	0.2090	0.1938
10	0.9053	0.8203	0.7441	0.6756	0.6139	0.5584	0.5083	0.4632	0.4224	0.3855	0.3522	0.3220	0.2946	0.2697	0.2472	0.2267	0.2080	0.1911	0.1756	0.1615
11	0.8963	0.8043	0.7224	0.6496	0.5847	0.5268	0.4751	0.4289	0.3875	0.3505	0.3173	0.2875	0.2607	0.2366	0.2149	0.1954	0.1778	0.1619	0.1476	0.1346
12	0.8874	0.7885	0.7014	0.6246	0.5568	0.4970	0.4440	0.3971	0.3555	0.3186	0.2858	0.2567	0.2307	0.2076	0.1869	0.1685	0.1520	0.1372	0.1240	0.1122
13	0.8787	0.7730	0.6810	0.6006	0.5303	0.4688	0.4150	0.3677	0.3262	0.2897	0.2575	0.2292	0.2042	0.1821	0.1625	0.1452	0.1299	0.1163	0.1042	0.0935
14	0.8700	0.7579	0.6611	0.5775	0.5051	0.4423	0.3878	0.3405	0.2992	0.2633	0.2320	0.2046	0.1807	0.1597	0.1413	0.1252	0.1110	0.0985	0.0876	0.0779
15	0.8613	0.7430	0.6419	0.5553	0.4810	0.4173	0.3624	0.3152	0.2745	0.2394	0.2090	0.1827	0.1599	0.1401	0.1229	0.1079	0.0949	0.0835	0.0736	0.0649
16	0.8528	0.7284	0.6232	0.5339	0.4581	0.3936	0.3387	0.2919	0.2519	0.2176	0.1883	0.1631	0.1415	0.1229	0.1069	0.0930	0.0811	0.0708	0.0618	0.0541
17	0.8444	0.7142	0.6050	0.5134	0.4363	0.3714	0.3166	0.2703	0.2311	0.1978	0.1696	0.1456	0.1252	0.1078	0.0929	0.0802	0.0693	0.0600	0.0520	0.0451
18	0.8360	0.7002	0.5874	0.4936	0.4155	0.3503	0.2959	0.2502	0.2120	0.1799	0.1528	0.1300	0.1108	0.0946	0.0808	0.0691	0.0592	0.0508	0.0437	0.0376
19	0.8277	0.6864	0.5703	0.4746	0.3957	0.3305	0.2765	0.2317	0.1945	0.1635	0.1377	0.1161	0.0981	0.0829	0.0703	0.0596	0.0506	0.0431	0.0367	0.0313
20	0.8195	0.6730	0.5537	0.4564	0.3769	0.3118	0.2584	0.2145	0.1784	0.1486	0.1240	0.1037	0.0868	0.0728	0.0611	0.0514	0.0433	0.0365	0.0308	0.0261
21	0.8114	0.6598	0.5375	0.4388	0.3589	0.2942	0.2415	0.1987	0.1637	0.1351	0.1117	0.0926	0.0768	0.0638	0.0531	0.0443	0.0370	0.0309	0.0259	0.0217
22	0.8034	0.6468	0.5219	0.4220	0.3418	0.2775	0.2257	0.1839	0.1502	0.1228	0.1007	0.0826	0.0680	0.0560	0.0462	0.0382	0.0316	0.0262	0.0218	0.0181
23	0.7954	0.6342	0.5067	0.4057	0.3256	0.2618	0.2109	0.1703	0.1378	0.1117	0.0907	0.0738	0.0601	0.0491	0.0402	0.0329	0.0270	0.0222	0.0183	0.0151
24	0.7876	0.6217	0.4919	0.3901	0.3101	0.2470	0.1971	0.1577	0.1264	0.1015	0.0817	0.0659	0.0532	0.0431	0.0349	0.0284	0.0231	0.0188	0.0154	0.0126
25	0.7798	0.6095	0.4776	0.3751	0.2953	0.2330	0.1842	0.1460	0.1160	0.0923	0.0736	0.0588	0.0471	0.0378	0.0304	0.0245	0.0197	0.0160	0.0129	0.0105
26	0.7720	0.5976	0.4637	0.3607	0.2812	0.2198	0.1722	0.1352	0.1064	0.0839	0.0663	0.0525	0.0417	0.0331	0.0264	0.0211	0.0169	0.0135	0.0109	0.0087
27	0.7644	0.5859	0.4502	0.3468	0.2678	0.2074	0.1609	0.1252	0.0976	0.0763	0.0597	0.0469	0.0369	0.0291	0.0230	0.0182	0.0144	0.0115	0.0091	0.0073
28	0.7568	0.5744	0.4371	0.3335	0.2551	0.1956	0.1504	0.1159	0.0895	0.0693	0.0538	0.0419	0.0326	0.0255	0.0200	0.0157	0.0123	0.0097	0.0077	0.0061
29	0.7493	0.5631	0.4243	0.3207	0.2429	0.1846	0.1406	0.1073	0.0822	0.0630	0.0485	0.0374	0.0289	0.0224	0.0174	0.0135	0.0105	0.0082	0.0064	0.0051
30	0.7419	0.5521	0.4120	0.3083	0.2314	0.1741	0.1314	0.0994	0.0754	0.0573	0.0437	0.0334	0.0256	0.0196	0.0151	0.0116	0.0090	0.0070	0.0054	0.0042

Table 13.3 Cumulative discount factors present value of a series of n regular annual payments, at an interest rate of I%: $c = \{1 - [(1 + I)^{-n}]\} / I$

Years	Discount factor for stated annual interest rate (%)														
	1	2	3	4	5	6	7	8	9	10	11	12	13	14	15
1	0.9901	0.9804	0.9709	0.9615	0.9524	0.9434	0.9346	0.9259	0.9174	0.9091	0.9009	0.8929	0.8850	0.8772	0.8696
2	1.9704	1.9416	1.9135	1.8861	1.8594	1.8334	1.8080	1.7833	1.7591	1.7355	1.7125	1.6901	1.6681	1.6467	1.6257
3	2.9410	2.8839	2.8286	2.7751	2.7232	2.6730	2.6243	2.5771	2.5313	2.4869	2.4437	2.4018	2.3612	2.3216	2.2832
4	3.9020	3.8077	3.7171	3.6299	3.5460	3.4651	3.3872	3.3121	3.2397	3.1699	3.1024	3.0373	2.9745	2.9137	2.8550
5	4.8534	4.7135	4.5797	4.4518	4.3295	4.2124	4.1002	3.9927	3.8897	3.7908	3.6959	3.6048	3.5172	3.4331	3.3522
6	5.7955	5.6014	5.4172	5.2421	5.0757	4.9173	4.7665	4.6229	4.4859	4.3553	4.2305	4.1114	3.9975	3.8887	3.7845
7	6.7282	6.4720	6.2303	6.0021	5.7864	5.5824	5.3893	5.2064	5.0330	4.8684	4.7122	4.5638	4.4226	4.2883	4.1604
8	7.6517	7.3255	7.0197	6.7327	6.4632	6.2098	5.9713	5.7466	5.5348	5.3349	5.1461	4.9676	4.7988	4.6389	4.4873
9	8.5660	8.1622	7.7861	7.4353	7.1078	6.8017	6.5152	6.2469	5.9952	5.7590	5.5370	5.3282	5.1317	4.9464	4.7716
10	9.4713	8.9826	8.5302	8.1109	7.7217	7.3601	7.0236	6.7101	6.4177	6.1446	5.8892	5.6502	5.4262	5.2161	5.0188
11	10.3676	9.7868	9.2526	8.7605	8.3064	7.8869	7.4987	7.1390	6.8052	6.4951	6.2065	5.9377	5.6869	5.4527	5.2337
12	11.2551	10.5753	9.9540	9.3851	8.8633	8.3838	7.9427	7.5361	7.1607	6.8137	6.4924	6.1944	5.9176	5.6603	5.4206
13	12.1337	11.3484	10.6350	9.9856	9.3936	8.8527	8.3577	7.9038	7.4869	7.1034	6.7499	6.4235	6.1218	5.8424	5.5831
14	13.0037	12.1062	11.2961	10.5631	9.8986	9.2950	8.7455	8.2442	7.7862	7.3667	6.9819	6.6282	6.3025	6.0021	5.7245
15	13.8651	12.8493	11.9379	11.1184	10.3797	9.7122	9.1079	8.5595	8.0607	7.6061	7.1909	6.8109	6.4624	6.1422	5.8474
16	14.7179	13.5777	12.5611	11.6523	10.8378	10.1059	9.4466	8.8514	8.3126	7.8237	7.3792	6.9740	6.6039	6.2651	5.9542
17	15.5623	14.2919	13.1661	12.1657	11.2741	10.4773	9.7632	9.1216	8.5436	8.0216	7.5488	7.1196	6.7291	6.3729	6.0472
18	16.3983	14.9920	13.7535	12.6593	11.6896	10.8276	10.0591	9.3719	8.7556	8.2014	7.7016	7.2497	6.8399	6.4674	6.1280
19	17.2260	15.6785	14.3238	13.1339	12.0853	11.1581	10.3356	9.6036	8.9501	8.3649	7.8393	7.3658	6.9380	6.5504	6.1982
20	18.0456	16.3514	14.8775	13.5903	12.4622	11.4699	10.5940	9.8181	9.1285	8.5136	7.9633	7.4694	7.0248	6.6231	6.2593
21	18.8570	17.0112	15.4150	14.0292	12.8212	11.7641	10.8355	10.0168	9.2922	8.6487	8.0751	7.5620	7.1016	6.6870	6.3125
22	19.6604	17.6580	15.9369	14.4511	13.1630	12.0416	11.0612	10.2007	9.4424	8.7715	8.1757	7.6446	7.1695	6.7429	6.3587
23	20.4558	18.2922	16.4436	14.8568	13.4886	12.3034	11.2722	10.3711	9.5802	8.8832	8.2664	7.7184	7.2297	6.7921	6.3988
24	21.2434	18.9139	16.9355	15.2470	13.7986	12.5504	11.4693	10.5288	9.7066	8.9847	8.3481	7.7843	7.2829	6.8351	6.4338
25	22.0232	19.5235	17.4131	15.6221	14.0939	12.7834	11.6536	10.6748	9.8226	9.0770	8.4217	7.8431	7.3300	6.8729	6.4641
26	22.7952	20.1210	17.8768	15.9828	14.3752	13.0032	11.8258	10.8100	9.9290	9.1609	8.4881	7.8957	7.3717	6.9061	6.4906
27	23.5596	20.7069	18.3270	16.3296	14.6430	13.2105	11.9867	10.9352	10.0266	9.2372	8.5478	7.9426	7.4086	6.9352	6.5135
28	24.3164	21.2813	18.7641	16.6631	14.8981	13.4062	12.1371	11.0511	10.1161	9.3066	8.6016	7.9844	7.4412	6.9607	6.5335
29	25.0658	21.8444	19.1885	16.9837	15.1411	13.5907	12.2777	11.1584	10.1983	9.3696	8.6501	8.0218	7.4701	6.9830	6.5509
30	25.8077	22.3965	19.6004	17.2920	15.3725	13.7648	12.4090	11.2578	10.2737	9.4269	8.6938	8.0552	7.4957	7.0027	6.5660

13.9.2.4 More advanced techniques

In addition to the techniques described in the previous sections there are many more complex methods used by accountancy experts. A number of these allow risk to be taken into account. One method, the 'capital asset pricing model', relates the the risk of a particular course of action to the return on a similar investment in relatively stable sections of the financial markets. It requires knowledge of the general level of risk acceptable to, say, a maintenance contractor so that the effect of accepting a higher level of risk for a new activity can be estimated. Details of advanced techniques can be found in the *Handbook of management accounting*[18].

Another technique takes account of a private company's mix of debt and equity and its gearing (the ratio of long-term debt to capital employed). This can be used to calculate a weighted average cost of capital (WACC), which in turn can be used to determine a discount rate for investments of average risk and adjusted to reflect projects that represent different risks[19].

13.10 Life cycle costs

Life cycle costs are the combined total of capital and revenue costs for an item of plant or equipment throughout its useful life. Established life cycle costs for particular items have a number of uses, including:

— to aid design decisions regarding the selection of systems and their components

— to aid decisions as to whether to repair or replace specific plant items

— to appraise the effectiveness of a plant or system at the end of its life with a view to future replication of the desirable features, e.g. designing out maintenance activities, reducing or eradicating unplanned downtime, improving reliability and avoiding excessive maintenance expenditure.

The capital costs of building services systems will be a combination of the initial capital costs, the discounted replacement costs and any residual value (scrap) of items of equipment or other components of the system. The revenue costs are made up of the energy costs, the planned maintenance costs, the unplanned maintenance costs and the costs associated with consequential losses resulting from plant failure, such as loss of occupant productivity or production plant downtime.

Obviously some elements of life cycle costs for specific systems cannot be accurately predicted and certain assumptions will always have to be made. It is unfortunate that very few data are available for typical failures and reliability of equipment and system components or for the maintenance costs associated with different systems.

References

1 *Facilities management measurement protocol* BIFM Best Practice Guide (Saffron Walden: British Institute of Facilities Management)

2 Smith M H *Maintenance and utility costs: results of a survey* BSRIA Technical Memoranda **TM3/91** (Bracknell: Building Services Research and Information Association) (1991)

3 *Spon's mechanical and electrical services price book* (30th edn.) (London: E & F N Spon) (published annually)

4 Building cost survey: Commercial offices (urban environment) *Building Services* **17**(9) 17–18 (September 1995)

5 Building cost survey: Commercial offices (non-urban environment) *Building Services* **17**(11) 15–16 (November 1995)

6 Building cost survey: Shopping centres *Building Services* **18**(1) 17–18 (January 1996)

7 Building cost survey: IT cabling *Building Services* **18**(3) 11–13 (March 1996)

8 Building cost survey: Theatres *Building Services* **18**(5) 16–17 (May 1996)

9 Building cost survey: Schools *Building Services* **18**(9) 11–13 (September 1996)

10 Building cost survey: Swimming pools *Building Services* **18**(11) 15–16 (November 1996)

11 Building cost survey: Combined heat and power (CHP) *Building Services* **19**(1) 17–18 (January 1997)

12 Building cost survey: Private hospitals *Building Services* **19**(3) 13–14 (March 1997)

13 Building cost survey: Commercial restaurants (provincial city centres) *Building Services* **19**(8) 13–14 (August 1997)

14 Building cost survey: Art galleries and museums *Building Services* **19**(11) 17–18 (November 1997)

15 Building cost survey: Lifts and escalators *Building Services* **20**(1) 17–18 (January 1998)

16 Building cost survey: Building energy management systems *Building Services* **20**(5) 19–20 (1998)

17 Building cost survey: Kitchens and serveries *Building Services* **20**(7) 28–30 (July 1997)

18 Innes J *Handbook of management accounting* [London: Chartered Institute of Management Accountants/Gee Publishing) (1998)

19 Ferry D J O and Flanagan R *Life cycle costing — a radical approach* CIRIA Report **122** (London: Construction Industry Research and Information Association) (1991)

Bibliography

Energy management (chapter 32); Owning and operating costs (chapter 33); and Operation and management (chapter 35) in *HVAC Applications* ASHRAE Handbook (Atlanta GA: American Society of Heating, Refrigeration and Air Conditioning Engineers) (1995)

IESNA Lighting Handbook (New York NY: Illuminating Engineering Society of North America) (2000)

CIBSE Code for interior lighting (London: Chartered Institution of Building Services Engineers) (1994)

BS 3811: 1993: Glossary of terms used in terotechnology (London: British Standards Institution) (1993)

BS 3843: 1992: Guide to terotechnology (the economic management of assets): Part 3: Guide to available techniques (London: British Standards Institution) (1992)

Williams B *Facilities economics* (Bromley: Building Economics Bureau) (1994)

Office service charge annual review (OSCAR) Jones Lang Wotton special report 1998 (London: Jones Lang Wotton) (1998)

14 Economic life factors

Contents

Summary

The tabulated data for this section comprise code numbers for different types of building services plant and equipment and a series of estimates of the economic life of constituent components.

The sources and derivation of the economic life estimates are detailed and a number of factors that can influence the life are explained.

Arrangements for the allocation of funding for plant replacement by the sinking fund method and a commercial refinement of this are described.

A graphical illustration and explanation of the staged, partial replacement of plant is provided together with details of depreciation and statutes covering capital allowances.

This section covers the use of economic life factors and replaces Table B18.2 (Life factors for mechanical and electrical plant) in CIBSE Guide B[1].

Economic life factors are an integral part of life cycle costing and the following principles should be followed:

(*a*) Compare alternative design solutions.

(*b*) Replace plant items and components at intervals which, for the purpose of prediction, should be the economic life factors. A system may comprise many plant items and components with various individual life cycles. This approach should ensure that a system operates at optimum performance.

(*c*) When commencing a new design, improvement or refurbishment, consider the total cost including design, safety, installation, testing, commissioning, satisfactory level of handover, maintenance, review of performance following handover, subsequent replacement and disposal.

Economic life factors for lifts are being developed for the second edition of CIBSE Guide D *Transportation systems in buildings*[2] and are not reproduced here. Note also that specialist industrial refrigeration plant and refrigeration equipment used in supermarkets and public houses for food and drink are not covered.

The economic life factors scheduled in this section are for initial reference and guidance only. Detailed information should always be obtained from the supplier, distributor, manufacturer, installer or professional adviser.

14.1 Background

To establish the economic life factors used in this section, information in published material[1, 3–11] was reviewed. In addition, advice and comments from the sources listed in the acknowledgements for this section were considered and, where appropriate, used in the text or economic life factor tables. In reviewing such a large amount of information a certain degree of flexibility has been necessary in the description of the equipment items. Where there is considered to be a need to review any particular item in greater detail, reference to the original source is recommended.

Readers should note that the economic life factors scheduled in this section are derived from a broadly based survey of generic plant and equipment. Users of the data may, however, wish to adjust the factors given based on their own experience or, in the case of particular proprietary equipment, to take advice from the manufacturer.

Kirk and Dell'Isola[11] define economic life, technological life and useful life of an item as:

— economic life: the estimated number of years until that item no longer represents the least expensive method of performing its function

— technological life: the estimated number of years until technology causes an item to become obsolete.

— useful life: the estimated number of years during which an item will perform its function according to some established performance standard.

The above definition of economic life has been used for the purposes of the life factors in this section. The definitions for technological life and useful life are provided for when comparing life factor schedules in other publications. It is important that contractual and legal documentation clearly define the basis of the life factors used to minimise misunderstanding and possible future disputes between the parties scheduled in the documentation.

The listed economic life factors assume that the following conditions apply:

- a good standard of maintenance (see CIBSE Technical Memoranda TM17 *Building services maintenance management*[12])
- a high standard of quality control at all levels during manufacture
- approved British and European standards and codes of practice are complied with
- installation, including testing and commissioning, has been to good industry standards (see CIBSE *Commissioning Codes*[13–17])
- where plant and equipment are imported from outside the European Union, equivalent quality and safety standards are clearly specified and appropriate inspections made
- hours of plant operation (especially rotating plant): many buildings are now being used for longer periods of time as commercial pressures and international competition intensify; where duplicate or multiple plant is installed, the hours of each unit should be assumed to be nominally equal
- adequate space for safety, access, maintenance and removal of plant (see *Space requirements for plant access, operation and maintenance*[18]).

14.2 Variation factors

Appropriate variation of the scheduled economic life factors can be made by applying a variation factor with a value greater or less than 1.0. A suggested range of conditions, together with typical examples that may require a variation factor to be applied, is listed below.

14.2.1 Condition 1: external environment

A factor should be applied in the following circumstances:

- urban developments where exposure to pollution and corrosion may occur
- rooftop exposure to rain, snow and wind
- coastal conditions, such as wind and exposure to salt-laden air.

14.2.2 Condition 2: internal environment

Dry and corrosion-free conditions are required for plant, equipment and distribution systems. Where this condition has not been met a variation factor may be appropriate.

14.2.3 Condition 3: technology changes

Software and communications technology changes may influence early replacement. For instance, improved user functionality as a result of using low-cost fibre optic technology which would affect an item's useful life.

14.2.4 Condition 4: design and specification

Commercial buildings, especially those constructed in the 1980s, may show a marked divergence between the design specification and the actual conditions observed (for occupants) or measured (relating to lighting and small power loads). This results from the increased use of computers and other items of office equipment now operated in commercial premises.

Studies instigated by BSRIA[19] and Stanhope[20, 21] have highlighted the matter of overdesign or overspecification which can give rise to operational problems in achieving acceptable comfort conditions. If a building falls into this category it is assumed that the systems will be recommissioned to suit the actual conditions, otherwise the control system may not be able to compensate and provide effective regulation of performance. This, in turn, can lead to 'hunting' (i.e. cycling between maximum and minimum output) leading to poor energy efficiency and a shorter plant and equipment lifespan than expected.

The general quality of materials, components, plant and equipment should, as a minimum requirement, comply with relevant British and European standards and codes of practice; where this is in doubt, a variation factor should be applied.

To avoid overspecification it is recommended that an action plan is prepared, based on BSRIA Technical Report TR21/95 *Over-engineering in building services*[22] and, for commercial developments, the British Council for Offices' *Best practice in the specification for offices*[23].

14.2.5 Condition 5: unoccupied and closed-down buildings

Where a building has been unoccupied or closed down for a number of years and is required to be used again, a condition survey is recommended (see section 16). Where appropriate, plant and systems should be repaired or refurbished and recommissioned to a satisfactory standard. Where this is not allowed, a factor variation for the residual life of the plant may well be appropriate.

Note that a condition survey may be relevant for either new or used plant and systems, especially where the purchase or lease of a building is under consideration.

14.2.6 Condition 6: maintenance

Where the standard of maintenance does not meet the criteria set out in CIBSE Technical Memoranda TM17[12], a variation factor should be applied.

14.2.7 Condition 7: hours of operation

The reference standard assumes a 12-hour operational period (Monday–Friday) and 8 hours during the weekend. If operating hours are higher or lower, a variation factor may be appropriate.

14.2.8 Condition 8: installation

The reference standard assumes that a high standard of installation quality control has been applied, approved British and European standards and codes of practice followed, and testing and commissioning have taken place[13-17]. A variation factor may be appropriate where there is some doubt that all these have occurred.

14.2.9 Condition 9: adequate space

Allowing adequate space for maintenance and plant replacement is very important; where the particular reference standard is in doubt, or plant and equipment have been 'shoe-horned' into a space, a variation factor will have to be applied[18].

14.2.10 Worked example

Assume that the reference standards for the conditions given in 14.2.6 and 14.2.9 have not been complied with, and variation factors of 0.95 and 0.92 have been adopted, the estimated economic life factor would be calculated as follows:

Reference economic life factor $= 20$ years

Estimated economic life factor $= 20 \times 0.95 \times 0.92$

$= 17.48$ years

It is important to appreciate that this method is subjective, and relies on assessment by trained and experienced engineers. Nevertheless, it provides a logical approach for estimating purposes; furthermore, the means of arriving at the chosen life factor is clearly defined and demonstrable.

14.3 Economic life factor codes and schedules

The economic life factors are arranged into groups (for example, refrigeration plant, boiler plant and open-type cooling towers) and each group given a code number (see Appendix 14.A1). Illustrations and technical information related to some equipment items can be found in the current *Opus building services design file*[24] using the extensive index. Figure 14.1 illustrates a building management control system (BMS), bringing together the equipment items scheduled under code 115. Figure 14.2 illustrates how, as

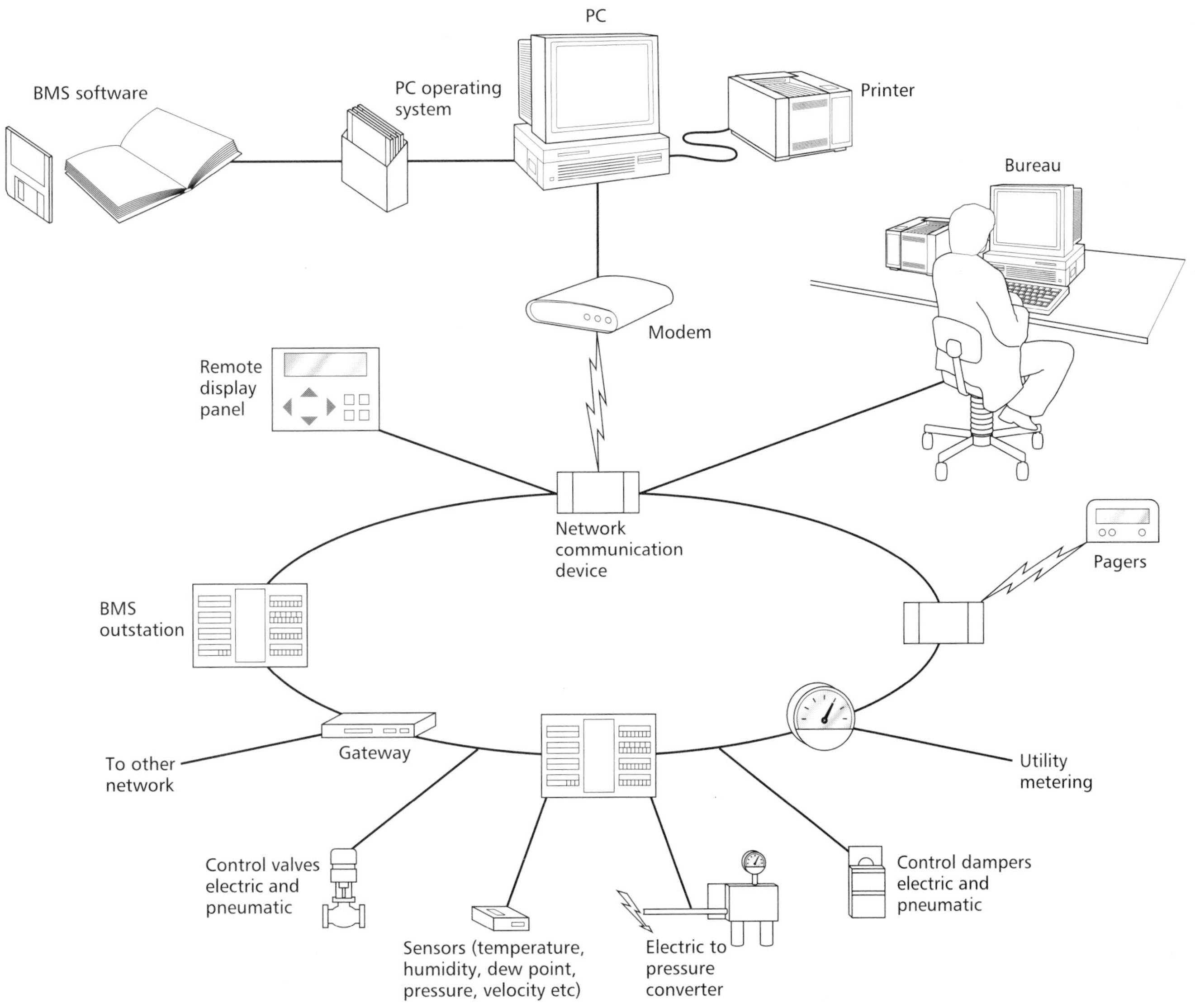

Figure 14.1 Equipment items coded 115 in a building management system and control system (reproduced by courtesy of E-Squared Ltd)

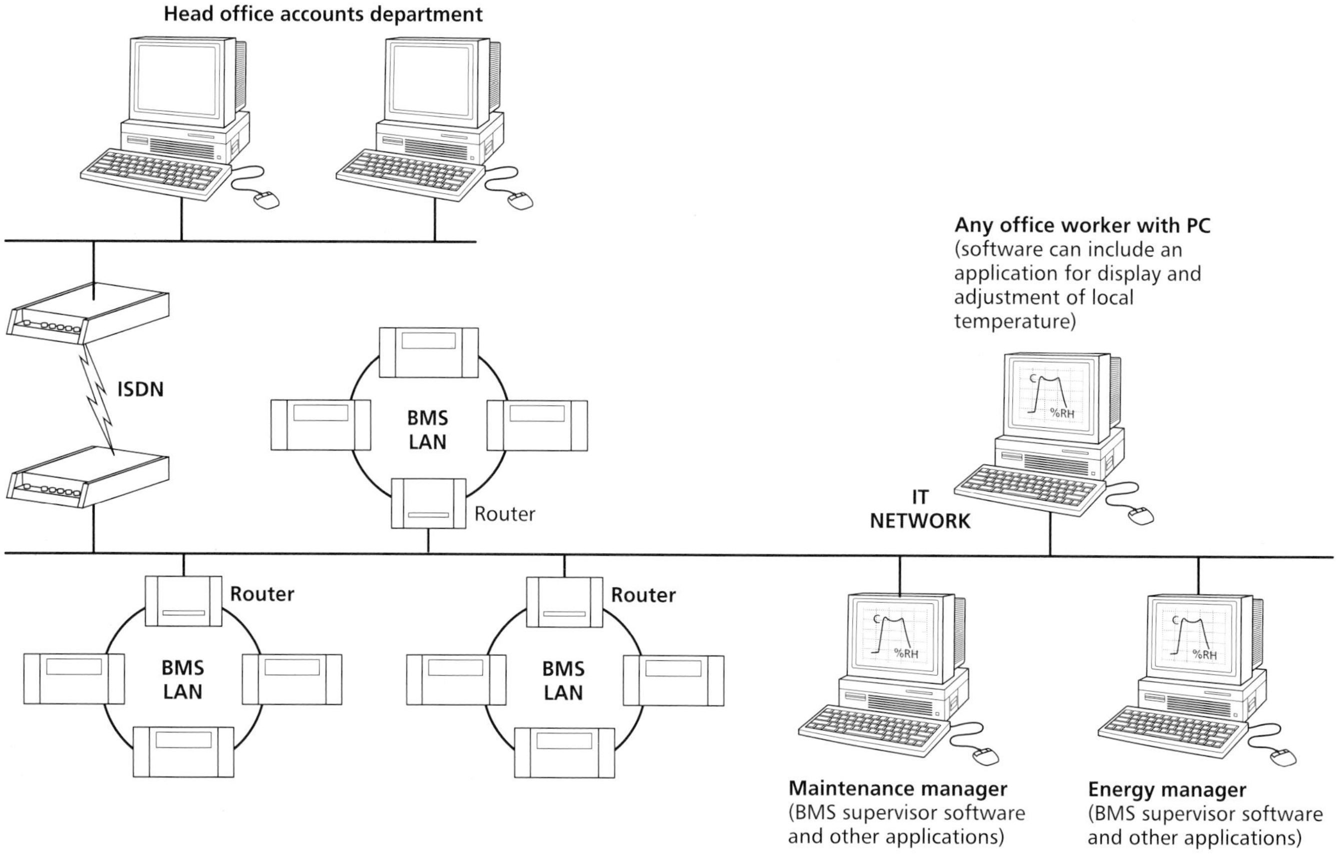

Figure 14.2 Integration of information technology (IT) and building management control system (BMS) technology[25] (reproduced by courtesy of *M&E Design*)

technology progresses, BMS technology and information technology (IT) are becoming integrated[25].

Appendix 14.A1 lists the complete economic life factor schedule. It should be noted that this is not exhaustive, and there will always be scope for additions and the need to recognise changes in technology.

14.4 Applications

14.4.1 Sinking fund

An approach to allocating funds for future plant and system replacement is to set up a sinking fund. In practice, this approach will need specialist accounting, tax and legal advice. This section concentrates on the calculations involved and ignores all possible effects of tax and inflation.

A sinking fund can be considered as a method of depreciation; at the end of the asset's life, the investment will provide cash equal to the cost of the asset. The general formula is:

$$AR = (RC \times I) / \{[(1+I)^n] - 1\}$$

Where AR is annual recovery (£), RC is replacement cost (£), I is annual interest rate (%) and n is life period (years).

Consider the replacement cost of boiler plant and system in 20 years' time at 4% yearly interest. The estimated cost is £37 400. What is the annual recovery and contribution to the sinking fund?

$$AR = (37\,400 \times 0.04) / \{[(1 + 0.04)^{20}] - 1\}$$

$$AR = £1256$$

It is important to demonstrate reasonably reliable economic life factors and the effect on the annual recovery should the factors be inaccurate. For example, if the actual life period were 13 rather than 20 years, using the same calculation procedure the annual recovery should have been set at £2249, a shortfall of £993 per annum.

14.4.2 Commercial method

For commercial purposes a more practical approach is required than simple sinking fund calculations. The method, as used in the property industry, is detailed as a worked example in Table 14.1. It covers a six-year period to illustrate the method in tabular form, using the same data as the example in section 14.4.1.

The principles of this practical, commercial method are:

(*a*) Depending on the level of inflation and market conditions, valuations should be obtained at periodic intervals from independent engineers to establish the likely replacement cost and should include a review of the original estimated life period (factor) for the plant and systems. These figures should be adjusted to allow for fees and value-added tax (VAT). The time period between valuations will typically be 2–3 years if inflation levels are high and 5–7 years if inflation is stable and reasonably low. Between valuations, appropriate yearly cost inflation indices should be obtained from independent sources based on their detailed knowledge of the industry, type of plant and system. These indices should then be compared with the retail prices index (RPI), which is well established and understood fully by financial professionals.

(*b*) The replacement cost of each plant item and system should be multiplied by the expired life period and divided by the expected life period to produce the expected provision. The provisions actually recovered to date should be deducted from the expected total provision to give a value representing the amount that has to be set aside to provide an adequate sum for the future replacement of the specific plant and system.

(*c*) The replacement costs should be adjusted each year for inflation based on independent advice. An annual contribution should be obtained by subtracting the expected provision from the previous year's provision figure.

(*d*) A notional interest allowance should be made on the previous year's expected provision, which represents the cumulative payments expected to have been received. This interest amount should then be deducted from the annual provision and the remaining balance is recovered from the tenants.

(*e*) A gross rate of interest allowance is calculated on the average bank base rate and is subject to tax deduction to meet the following conditions:

- the replacement provision is recovered as additional rent, which is taxable
- interest can be earned only on amounts retained after deducting the appropriate rate of corporation tax
- tax will then be applied again on interest received (i.e. two levels of tax need to be applied).

(*f*) Replacement provisions should be retained in a general provision account and not be treated as part of company income.

(*g*) When a plant and system replacement becomes due the landlord will, in general, be required to make good any shortfall in funds (which can arise as a result of unlet spaces, lease defects, service charge capping and the like).

(*h*) Shortfalls relating to tenants in occupation at the time of replacement would be included in the service charge in the year following replacement of the plant and system.

(*i*) Where there is an overprovision of funds, nothing more is collected until the reserve and replacement cost balance (based on revaluation criteria) come near to convergence.

(*j*) Where there is an underprovision of funds, it may be necessary to try to recover the shortfall in the year of revaluation. This would be subject to commercial considerations and may be spread over two or three years.

14.4.3 Partial replacement during expected life period

Figure 14.3 illustrates how the value of plant and system will change should early replacement be introduced due to changes in technology and energy management. The following data are used in conjunction with the example in section 14.4.1.

(*a*) The plant and system are assumed to reduce in value on a linear basis over a 20-year period with zero value at the end of the life period.

(*b*) In year 10, the control system is upgraded at a cost of £5000 with a high probability of upgrading again in a further 10 years, indicated by the solid line. The dashed line indicates an upgrade with extended life after 10 years.

(*c*) In year 15, a new energy management system is introduced at a cost of £4000 which is likely to last for a further 5 years, indicated in black, before work will be required again. The dashed line indicates an upgrade with extended life after 5 years.

This is a simple model but could be developed to introduce non-linear yearly changes in value and inflation by extending the life period beyond 20 years with the introduction of modernisation and refurbishment. This approach could satisfy the need for reducing operating and maintenance costs and keeping plant and systems as modern and energy efficient as possible.

14.4.4 Depreciation

Accounting standards define depreciation(26), but for all practical purposes the following details must be determined for each item of plant or equipment before any assessment can be made:

- the total cost (£)
- economic life (years)
- salvage value (£)

Table 14.1 Example calculation using commercial method

Year ending	Life (years)	Past life (years)	Interest rate (%)	Inflation rate (%)	Replacement cost (£)	Reserve (£)	Past recovery (£)	Annual recovery (£)	Interest allowance (£)	Contribution (£)
1992	20	1	5.00	6.00	37 400	1 870	—	1870	—	1870
1993	20	2	3.80	4.00	38 896	3 890	1 870	2020	71	1949
1994	20	3	2.30	3.80	40 374	6 056	3 890	2167	89	2077
1995	20	4	2.59	3.00	41 585	8 317	6 056	2261	157	2104
1996	20	5	3.00	4.00	43 249	10 812	8 317	2495	250	2246
1997	20	6	3.00	4.00	44 979	13 494	10 812	2681	324	2357

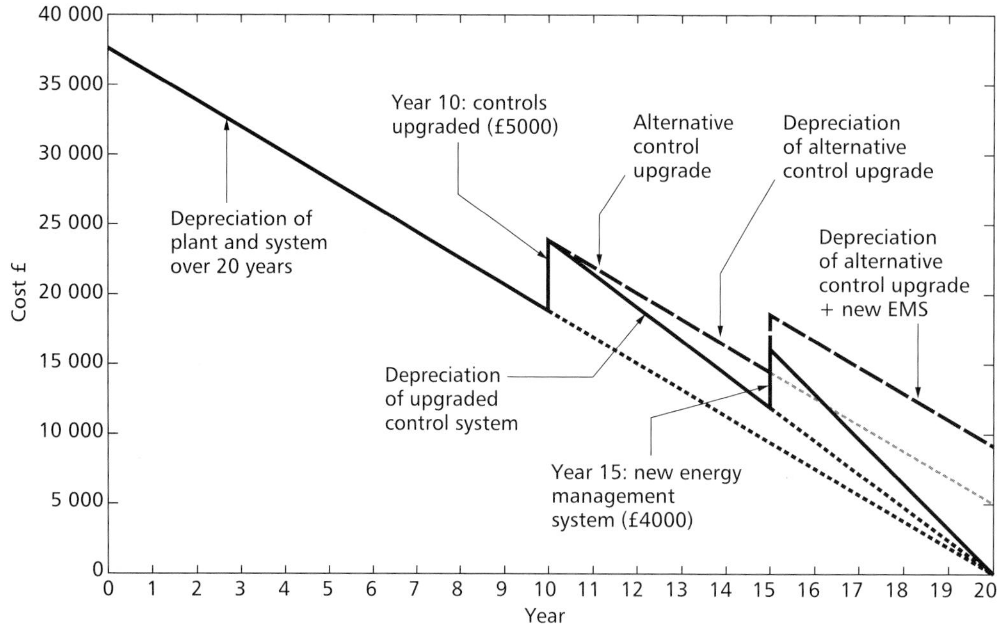

Figure 14.3 Changing value of plant resulting from early replacement

— a method of depreciation which is systematic and rational.

The building services engineer can establish values for total cost, economic life and salvage value while the accountant decides the depreciation method. Various depreciation methods are scheduled as follows:

— straight line

— sum of the year's digits

— fixed percentage

— compound

— declining balance

— sinking fund

— repair reserve

— revaluation

— manufacturing unit.

14.4.5 Investment appraisal

Investment appraisal is dealt with in section 13.9.2 but economic life factor input is needed before any meaningful appraisal can be made.

14.4.6 Capital allowances and the Finance Act 1997

When machinery or plant is purchased for a business, the cost of each item is added to a pool (motor vehicles are treated separately). A yearly capital allowance of 25% on a reducing balance basis is applied for each tax year to the pool and claimed as a writing-down allowance. Schedule 14 of the *Finance Act 1997*[27] amended the *Capital Allowances Act 1990* by introducing the case of machinery or plant that is new or, when new, would have a useful economic life of at least 25 years; a 6% capital allowance then applies on the reducing balance basis. There are exclusions to this new rule and reference should be made to the *Finance Act 1997* for further information; current investment allowances made in budgets subsequent to the Act should also be identified and applied.

The items of machinery or plant that qualify for capital allowances can be complex and assessing them requires the expertise of tax, quantity surveying and engineering professionals.

The other engineering input to the above considerations would involve the assessment of economic life periods and, where appropriate, the provision of assessments for the Inland Revenue Inspector.

References

1 *Installation and equipment data* CIBSE Guide B (London: Chartered Institution of Building Services Engineers) (1986)

2 *Transportation systems in buildings* CIBSE Guide D (2nd edn.) (London: Chartered Institution of Building Services Engineers) (in preparation)

3 Estimates of service lives of various system components (Table 3) In *HVCA Applications* ASHRAE Handbook (Atlanta GA: American Society of Heating, Refrigerating and Air Conditioning Engineers) (1995)

4 *Periods of use and maintenance costs, based on the fundamentals of Sanitar Und Heizungstechnik* Publication 2067 of the VDI (German Society of Engineers) BSRIA Translation No. **256**, Report **76230/1** (Bracknell: Building Services Research and Information Association) (1985)

5 Martin P L and Oughton D R *Faber and Kell's heating and air-conditioning of buildings* (8th edn.) (Oxford: Butterworth-Heinemann Ltd) (1995)

6 *Maintenance of mechanical services* (London: Department of Education and Science/The Stationery Office) (1990)

7 *Maintenance of electrical services* (London: Department of Education and Science/The Stationery Office) (1992)

8 *HAPM component life manual* (London: E & F N Spon) (1992)

9 *Anticipated economic life expectancy of MPS building services* MPS Report **M.203** (London: Metropolitan Police Service, Property

Services Department Surveying and Engineering Division) (1996)

10 Jønsson A and Lindgren S *The longevity of building services installations Stage 1: Inventory of operating experiences for estimating longevity* Report 811662 4/80s of Swedish Building Research Council BSRIA Translation No **252** (Bracknell: Building Services Research and Information Association)

11 Kirk S J and Dell'Isola A J *Life cycle costing for design professionals* (New York: McGraw-Hill) (1995)

12 *Building services maintenance management* CIBSE Technical Memoranda **TM17** (London: Chartered Institution of Building Services Engineers) (1994)

13 *Air distribution systems* CIBSE Commissioning Code A (London: Chartered Institution of Building Services Engineers) (1996)

14 *Boiler plant* CIBSE Commissioning Code B (London: Chartered Institution of Building Services Engineers) (1975)

15 *Automatic controls* CIBSE Commissioning Code C (London: Chartered Institution of Building Services Engineers) (1973)

16 *Refrigerating systems* CIBSE Commissioning Code R (London: Chartered Institution of Building Services Engineers) (1991)

17 *Water distribution systems* CIBSE Commissioning Code W (London: Chartered Institution of Building Services Engineers) (1994)

18 *Space requirements for plant access operation and maintenance* Defence Works Functional Standard: Design and Maintenance Guide **08** (London: Ministry of Defence/The Stationery Office) (1996)

19 Hejab M and Parsloe C *Small power loads* BSRIA Technical Note **TN8/92** (Bracknell: Building Services Research and Information Association) (1992)

20 LoPinto A, Farnfield T and Eames J *An assessment of small power loads for commercial office buildings* Stanhope Position Paper (London: Stanhope Properties) (1993)

21 Katsikakis D and Laing A *An assessment of occupation density levels in commercial office buildings* Stanhope Position Paper (London: Stanhope Properties) (1993)

22 Parsloe C J *Over-engineering in building services* BSRIA Technical Report **TR21/95** (Bracknell: Building Services Research and Information Association) (1995)

23 *Best practice in the specification for offices* (Reading: British Council for Offices) (1997)

24 *Opus building services design file* (London: Building Services Publications) (annual)

25 Monson C Sharing the information superhighway *M&E Design* 20–21 (July 1997)

26 Wood F and Sangster A *Business accounting 2* (7th edn.) (London: Pitman Publishing) (1996)

27 *Finance Act 1997* (London: The Stationery Office) (1997)

28 *Fire engineering* CIBSE Guide E (London: Chartered Institution of Building Services Engineers) (1997)

Appendix 14.A1: CIBSE economic life factor codes and schedules

This appendix contains CIBSE's economic life factor codes and a complete schedule for equipment. Note that this schedule will be subject to additions and changes and must therefore be kept under review.

Table 14.2 CIBSE economic life factor codes

Equipment/system	Code number
Boiler plant	100
Refrigeration plant — medium to large	101
Open type cooling towers	102
External heat rejection for refrigeration plant	103
Boiler plant auxiliaries	104
Water tanks	105
Ductwork systems and components	106
Air conditioning terminal units	107
Heating terminal units	108
Pipework systems and components	109
Drainage	110
Fire fighting and protection systems	111
Electrical distribution network	112
Electrical installations in buildings	113
Electrical generating plant	114
Building management & controls (electronic/electric)	115
Controls general	116
Miscellaneous electrical equipment and plant	117
Miscellaneous mechanical equipment and plant	118

Table 14.3 Economic life factors

Equipment item	CIBSE code	Life factor (years)	Remarks
Boiler plant			
Shell and tube boilers (steam and HTHW)	100	20 to 25	Water treatment is very important
Water tube boilers (steam and HTHW)	100	25 to 30	Water treatment is very important
Electrode/electric boilers (steam and HTHW)	100	15 to 20	Water treatment is very important
Shell and tube boilers (MTHW/LTHW)	100	15 to 20	
Water tube boilers (MTHW/LTHW)	100	15 to 20	
Electrode/electric boilers (MTHW/LTHW)	100	15 to 25	
Cast iron sectional boilers (MTHW/LTHW)	100	15 to 25	
Steel boilers (MTHW/LTHW)	100	15 to 20	
Condensing boilers (MTHW/LTHW)	100	15 to 20	
Refrigeration plant — medium to large			
Centrifugal chiller	101	15 to 20	See note 1
Reciprocating chiller	101	15 to 20	See note 1
Screw chiller	101	15 to 25	See note 1
Absorption chiller	101	15 to 20	
Open type cooling towers			
Plastic coated metal cooling tower	102	20 to 25	Consider thickness, bonding and quality of plastic coating
Galvanised metal cooling tower	102	10 to 15	Consider thickness and quality of galvanising
Timber constructed cooling tower	102	10 to 15	Consider quality of timber preservation which can extend life
Ceramic cooling tower	102	30 to 35	
Plastic constructed cooling tower	102	15 to 20	Consider thickness and quality of plastic
Epoxy treated metal cooling tower	102	10 to 15	
Stainless steel cooling tower	102	25 to 40	Consider quality and thickness of stainless steel
External heat rejection for refrigeration plant			
Air cooled condensers	103	15 to 20	
Evaporative condensers	103	15 to 20	
Air blast dry air coolers — plastic coated metal	103	25 to 30	Consider thickness, bonding and quality of plastic coating
Air blast dry air coolers — galvanised metal	103	15 to 25	Consider thickness and quality of galvanising
Air blast dry air coolers — epoxy treated metal	103	15 to 25	
Boiler plant auxiliaries			
Oil storage tanks — external protection	104	15 to 20	Depends on thickness of metal and corrosion protection
Oil storage tanks — underground	104	10 to 20	Depends on thickness of metal and corrosion protection

Table continues

Table 14.3 Economic life factors — *continued*

Equipment item	CIBSE code	Life factor (years)	Remarks
Combustion controls	104	15 to 20	
Boiler electrodes	104	5 to 10	
Feed pumps	104	15 to 20	
Water treatment	104	15 to 20	
Atmospheric gas burners	104	20 to 25	
Forced air gas burners	104	15 to 20	
Oil burners	104	15 to 20	
Solid fuel handling plant	104	10 to 15	Conveyor system up to 20 years
High temperature fans	104	15 to 25	
Instrumentation	104	10 to 20	
Oil distribution system for boiler plant	104	15 to 25	
Gas distribution system for boiler plant	104	20 to 25	
Mild steel flue	104	8 to 15	Depends on thickness of metal and corrosion protection
Stainless steel flue	104	15 to 25	Check quality of stainless steel
Brick or concrete chimney — external	104	35 to 40	
Brick or concrete chimney — internal	104	45 to 50	
Steel chimney — external	104	25 to 30	Depends on thickness of metal and corrosion protection
Water tanks			
Cast iron water cisterns	105	30 to 35	
Mild steel (treated) water cisterns	105	8 to 15	Not for domestic or drinking water purposes
Plastic water cisterns	105	30 to 35	High quality structural support is necessary
Galvanised metal water cisterns	105	10 to 15	
Ductwork systems and components			
Ductwork (galvanised)	106	25 to 35	
Ductwork (plastic)	106	15 to 20	Mechanical damage and expansion need to be considered
Ductwork (flexible circular)	106	20 to 25	Mechanical damage needs to be considered also cleaning difficulties
Fans (heavy duty centrifugal)	106	20 to 25	
Fans (centrifugal)	106	15 to 20	
Fans (axial)	106	15 to 20	
Fans (propeller)	106	10 to 15	
Fans (roof mounted units)	106	15 to 20	
Fire dampers: curtain type	106	10 to 15	
Coils (copper fins) heating	106	25 to 30	
Coils (copper fins) cooling	106	25 to 30	Consider operational duty — wet surfaces
Coils (aluminium fins) heating	106	15 to 20	Consider quality and thickness of aluminium fins and exposure to adverse external conditions
Coils (aluminium fins) cooling	106	15 to 20	Consider quality and thickness of aluminium fins and exposure to adverse and wet external conditions
Coils (galvanised) heating	106	12 to 15	
Spray cooler coils (copper electro-tinned) and washers	106	15 to 20	
Eliminators (galvanised)	106	8 to 12	
Eliminators (plastic)	106	12 to 18	
Eliminators (stainless steel)	106	15 to 25	
Coils (electric)	106	10 to 15	
Thermal wheels	106	15 to 20	
Filters (automatic) — excluding media	106	15 to 20	
Filters (panel) — excluding media	106	15 to 20	
Filters (electrostatic)	106	10 to 15	
Filters (activated carbon) — excluding media	106	15 to 20	
Grilles and diffusers (anodised aluminium)	106	25 to 30	
Grilles and diffusers (painted metal)	106	25 to 30	
Plate recuperator	106	20 to 30	
Dampers manual	106	15 to 20	
Dampers automatic	106	15 to 20	
Steam humidifier (direct)	106	10 to 15	Maintenance is very important
Steam humidifier (electric generated)	106	5 to 10	Maintenance is very important
Water spray humidifier	106	12 to 18	Early signs of corrosion must be dealt with
Pan type humidifier	106	8 to 12	Early signs of corrosion must be dealt with
Chemical dehumidifiers (excluding medium)	106	15 to 20	
External louvres (anodised aluminium)	106	20 to 30	Regular cleaning is important to avoid possible breakdown of surface coating

Table continues

Table 14.3 Economic life factors — *continued*

Equipment item	CIBSE code	Life factor (years)	Remarks
External louvres (steel painted)	106	15 to 25	Early signs of corrosion must be dealt with
Attenuators	106	15 to 25	Consider type of lining, adhesive and fixing of acoustic material
Packaged air handling/conditioning units (internal)	106	15 to 20	
Packaged air handling/conditioning units (external)	106	10 to 15	Consider type of corrosion protection
Air conditioning terminal units			
Fan coil units (heating and cooling)	107	12 to 15	
Induction units	107	20 to 25	
Terminal reheat units	107	20 to 25	
VAV terminal units (bellows type)	107	15 to 20	
VAV terminal units (box type)	107	15 to 20	
Fan assisted VAV terminal units	107	10 to 15	
Double duct terminal units	107	15 to 20	
Chilled ceiling panels	107	20 to 25	Flexible water pipework connections — depending on type 10 years
Chilled beams	107	20 to 25	Flexible water pipework connections — depending on type 10 years
Ventilated ceilings	107	25 to 30	
VRV units	107	10 to 15	
VVT fan powered terminal units	107	15 to 20	
Split systems	107	10 to 15	
Heating terminal units			
Radiators (cast iron)	108	20 to 25	
Radiators (steel)	108	10 to 15	Water condition is important
Radiators (2 mm thick steel)	108	20 to 25	Water condition is important
Radiators aluminium	108	15 to 20	Water condition is important and materials in the system
Radiator painting	108	5 to 8	Use correct type of paint
Unit heaters (steam and hot water)	108	15 to 20	
Unit heaters (gas and electric)	108	10 to 15	
Radiant heaters (steam and hot water)	108	20 to 25	
Radiant heaters (electric)	108	8 to 12	
Fan coil units (heating only)	108	12 to 18	
Natural convectors water	108	15 to 25	
Natural convectors electric	108	8 to 10	
Underfloor heating with concrete encased steel pipes	108	25 to 35	Suggest a long-term bonded warranty is obtained — corrosion prevention of steel pipes
Underfloor heating with concrete encased plastic pipes	108	25 to 40	Suggest a long-term bonded warranty is obtained — consider quality of plastic pipes
Underfloor electric heating	108	20 to 30	
Ceiling heating (hot water)	108	20 to 30	
Ceiling heating (electric)	108	15 to 20	
Electric storage heaters	108	10 to 15	
Pipework systems and components			
Open pipework systems (steel)	109	20 to 25	
Closed pipework systems (steel)	109	25 to 30	
Open pipework systems (copper)	109	30 to 35	Consider tube thickness and quality of copper
Closed pipework systems (copper)	109	40 to 45	Consider tube thickness and quality of copper
Open pipework systems (steel galvanised)	109	25 to 30	
Closed pipework systems (steel galvanised)	109	35 to 40	
Refrigerant pipework systems	109	20 to 30	See note 1
Steam pipework system	109	20 to 35	
Condensate pipework system	109	10 to 15	Consider type of material, wall thickness and water treatment
Condensate collecting vessel	109	10 to 15	Consider type of material, wall thickness and water treatment
Open expansion vessel	109	10 to 15	
Closed expansion vessel with membrane	109	15 to 20	
Water treatment plant	109	15 to 20	
Water treatment control and measurement equipment	109	8 to 20	
Pumps (base mounted)	109	20 to 25	
Pumps (pipework mounted)	109	15 to 20	
Pumps (glandless)	109	5 to 15	
Pumps (sump and well)	109	8 to 12	
Pumps (condensate)	109	10 to 15	
Bellows flexible (steel)	109	10 to 15	
Bellows flexible (rubber)	109	10 to 20	

Table continues

Table 14.3 Economic life factors — *continued*

Equipment item	CIBSE code	Life factor (years)	Remarks
Bellows expansion (steel)	109	10 to 20	
Valves (glandless)	109	20 to 25	
Valves (glands)	109	15 to 20	
Calorifiers	109	20 to 25	
Heat exchangers (shell and tube)	109	20 to 25	
Ductwork and vessel thermal insulation (blanket type)	109	15 to 20	Consider type of fixing and mechanical damage
Pipework and vessel thermal insulation (moulded type)	109	15 to 20	Consider fire and smoke rating
Drainage			
Internal waste, foul and rainwater drainage (cast iron)	110	30 to 35	
Internal waste, foul and rainwater drainage (copper)	110	35 to 40	
Internal waste, foul and rainwater drainage (plastic)	110	15 to 20	Consider possibility of mechanical damage and expansion
Below ground salt glazed drainage	110	30 to 40	Consider possibility of damage and structural movement
Below ground cast iron drainage	110	35 to 45	Consider possibility of ground and structural movement
Below ground plastic drainage	110	35 to 40	Consider mechanical damage
Fire fighting and protection systems			
Alternate wet and dry sprinklers	111	20	Consider corrosion; see CIBSE Guide E[28] section 8.1.7.3
Wet sprinklers	111	25 to 30	Consider corrosion
Wet risers	111	15 to 25	
Dry risers	111	25 to 40	
Foam systems	111	10 to 20	
Portable fire appliances	111	5 to 10	
Fire hose reels	111	15 to 20	
Fire hydrants	111	30 to 40	
Fire alarms (electrical)	111	20 to 25	
Fire dampers (curtain type)	111	10 to 15	
Computer room fire extinguishing system	111	15 to 20	Consider environmental impact and possible phasing out of fire extinguishing agent
Smoke detectors	111	10 to 15	
Electrical distribution network			
Switchgear and distribution equipment	112	20 to 25	
Transformers (dry type)	112	25 to 30	
Transformers (oil type)	112	25 to 30	
Mains cables (permanent installations)	112	25 to 30	
Electrical installations in buildings			
Final circuits and outlets	113	20 to 25	
Lighting installations (internal)	113	20 to 25	Low voltage decorative may be limited to 10 years
Lighting installations (external)	113	15 to 20	
Electrical motors (general)	113	15 to 20	Smaller motors may have a shorter life — check with supplier
Motor speed control devices	113	10 to 15	
Motor control centres	113	20 to 25	
Electrical generating plant			
Alternators	114	25 to 30	
Continuously rated gas/oil engines (frequent use)	114	15 to 20	
Continuously rated gas/oil engines (standby)	114	25 to 30	
Continuously rated steam engines (frequent use)	114	25 to 30	
Continuously rated steam turbines (frequent use)	114	25 to 35	
Building management and controls (electronic/electric)			
Personal computer	115	5 to 10	Alternative name — supervisor. Reference note 2.0
PC operating system	115	5 to 10	See note 2
BMS operating system	115	5 to 10	
Autodial modem	115	5 to 10	
Printer	115	5 to 10	With frequent use operating costs are important
Screened network (hardwiring)	115	25 to 30	Should be future proofed with additional cable wireways. See note 2
Network communication devices	115	10 to 15	Proprietary devices or gateways — may require support. See note 2
Damper actuators	115	10 to 15	
Intelligent outstations	115	5 to 15	See note 2
Sensors	115	3 to 10	Periodic loop tuning and calibration should be considered

Table continues

Table 14.3 Economic life factors — *continued*

Equipment item	CIBSE code	Life factor (years)	Remarks
Control valves	115	15 to 20	
Control dampers	115	15 to 20	
Electronic/pneumatic interfaces	115	10 to 15	
Utility metering	115	10 to 20	
Pagers	115	4 to 6	
Remote display panels	115	5 to 15	See note 2
Hardwiring between devices	115	25 to 30	Screened cables may be necessary
Controls general			
Pneumatic controls	116	15 to 20	
Electric controls	116	15 to 20	
Electronic controls	116	12 to 18	
Hydraulic valve actuators	116	10 to 15	
Pneumatic valve actuators	116	15 to 20	
Self-contained valve actuators	116	8 to 10	
Miscellaneous electrical equipment and plant			
Lead acid batteries (sealed)	117	3 to 10	
Nickel alkaline batteries (vented)	117	20 to 25	
Battery chargers	117	20 to 25	
Clock systems	117	20 to 25	
Communication systems	117	20 to 30	Voice and data. See note 2
Public address systems	117	20 to 25	
Intruder alarms and intercommunications	117	10 to 15	
Uninterrupted power supply systems	117	20 to 25	
Closed circuit television and video	117	10 to 15	
Television and satellite systems	117	15 to 20	See note 2
Lightning protection	117	25 to 30	
Lighting control and management system	117	15 to 20	
Continuous flow electrical heaters	117	12 to 15	
Electrical water heaters	117	12 to 15	
Electrical storage heaters with ventilation	117	20 to 25	
Electrical floor heating	117	20 to 30	
Electrical heater (on peak)	117	8 to 12	
Window unit air conditioner	117	8 to 10	
Residential single or split package air conditioner	117	10 to 15	
Commercial through the wall air conditioner	117	10 to 15	
Water cooled air conditioner	117	10 to 15	
Residential air to air heat pump	117	10 to 15	
Commercial air to air heat pump	117	10 to 15	
Commercial water to air heat pump	117	15 to 20	
Miscellaneous mechanical equipment and plant			
Kitchen (cooking and support systems)	118	15 to 20	
Laundries (equipment and support systems)	118	15 to 20	
Water features	118	10 to 15	Water treatment is very important
Computer room air conditioning	118	15 to 20	
Tea rooms (equipment and support systems)	118	15 to 20	
Hand dryers	118	5 to 10	
Drinking fountains	118	10 to 20	
Vending machines	118	5 to 10	
Sanitary towel disposal	118	10 to 15	
Food/container waste disposal	118	5 to 10	
Waste paper shredders/disposal	118	10 to 15	
Stair/lobby ventilation	118	15 to 25	
Fire protection (pipes and ducts)	118	15 to 25	Damage to fire protection should be examined at frequent intervals
Incinerators	118	15 to 20	
Gas or oil fired furnaces	118	15 to 20	Selection of heat exchanger material is important
Domestic gas fired warm air heaters	118	12 to 18	
Domestic gas fired boilers	118	15 to 20	
Domestic gas fired combination boilers	118	12 to 15	
Gas fired hot water (storage and continuous)	118	12 to 15	
Gas fires	118	8 to 12	

Note 1 The phasing out of CFCs and HCFCs may require replacement of equipment earlier than originally planned

Note 2 Technology changes can influence early replacement

Note 3 Ensure that all heat exchangers especially refrigerant cooling and heat pump systems are suitable for UK operating conditions

15 Maintenance audits

Contents

Summary

A technique for auditing maintenance contract performance is described in detail. It entails an assessment of performance under the headings of management, maintenance, communications, health and safety, technical proficiency and invoicing.

A qualitative scoring method is proposed and a procedure for conducting the audit is outlined.

An example maintenance audit check sheet is provided.

This section is intended to provide a formal framework to allow clients, maintenance contractors and professional advisers to work together to improve the quality of performance of engineering maintenance. It may also be used as a means of auditing a direct labour force.

A maintenance audit is always likely to be based on subjective assessments but the intention is that, by developing a standard format for the assessment document and describing the content of each item, the process can be made more objective. This should increase the benefit of the audit to all the parties concerned. If a client has any concerns about understanding or completing the maintenance audit document, it is strongly recommended that professional advice be obtained.

15.1 Audit document

A maintenance audit document is illustrated in Appendix 15.A1. The document should be completed by or in close cooperation with the client. The services of a professional adviser may be used where appropriate.

The initial information includes, for record purposes:

- details of the client
- type of maintenance contract
- contract start date
- building location
- date of the assessment
- name of maintenance contractor
- name of assessor.

Types of maintenance contract are detailed in section 4; they can include, for example, labour only, planned maintenance, call-out only, service level, fixed price, measured, semi-comprehensive, fully comprehensive and inspection-only contracts.

The audit document addresses the topics outlined below. These are not intended to be definitive, and the user may wish to modify the headings to suit a specific application.

15.2 Audit details

15.2.1 Management

This has two elements: client and contractor staff. The first addresses how the contract is being complied with, whether reports are submitted as required, whether meetings are scheduled and kept to, and how productive and positive these are. Contractors should be aware of their role in ensuring that buildings remain functional.

The second element, contractor staff, considers their quality, management and supervision, conduct and appearance, housekeeping, response to work requests, call-outs and emergencies, and standards of training. It is important for maintenance operatives to keep up to date with technical developments, safety awareness and practical training on the wide variety of plant likely to be encountered. Adequate opportunities for and the implementation of recognised training can be a significant indicator of a competent contractor.

15.2.2 Maintenance service

Planned preventive maintenance (PPM) is the systematic investigation at predetermined intervals of all the plant items listed on the asset register. This element assesses whether effective work planning is being applied, the PPM is being carried out at the stated intervals and all the tasks are being achieved to an acceptable quality standard. An important aspect of the contractor's management is to ensure that the maintenance periodicity is under continuous review to minimise tendencies towards either under- or overmaintenance.

In practical terms, it is recommended that the client or its adviser makes periodic inspections of plant rooms, the major occupied areas and equipment of significant importance to the normal building operation to monitor that satisfactory maintenance standards are being achieved. The inspections should include regular checks that all control equipment is within calibration.

The performance element also addresses whether the expected level of service is provided, the required plant availability is achieved, the level of complaints from the building occupants is acceptable, the response time to work requests and emergencies is satisfactory, and work is carried out in a positive manner. The latter includes showing an innovative, flexible approach, including initiative and perseverance.

15.2.3 Communication

Maintenance review meetings allow the client and contractor to develop a mutual understanding of their respective objectives and requirements. Minutes of each formal meeting should be produced for reference and to ensure that agreed actions are carried out. It may be appropriate for the contractor to prepare cost forecasts for some or all such meetings to demonstrate the anticipated progress of the contract.

Regular meetings should prevent situations getting out of hand by fostering improved working relationships. Typically, these meetings should take place at least quarterly (more frequently in the early stages of a contract). A typical agenda should include an indication of the current status of planned maintenance work, a summary of all instructions for additional work received in the last period and a report on work completed.

Communications cover those between client and contractor, and with the occupants of the building. Ideally, occupant complaints should be recorded formally with the client ascertaining the true nature of the complaint before handing over the matter to the contractor. All communications need to be clear and concise. Response time to instructions can also be addressed under this heading.

This element should reflect the ability of both parties to raise problems or concerns and discuss them in a positive manner, with the expectation of a high level of professional advice and guidance from the contractor.

15.2.4 Health and safety

Although the client must accept ultimate responsibility for health and safety, the implementation of specific procedures may be placed with the contractor. These aspects should be clearly identified at the start of the contract and monitored to ensure that the work is being carried out satisfactorily. Health and safety policy statements should be available from both the client and the contractor. These should be exchanged at the start of the contract and any anomalies resolved, particularly in respect to demarcation of responsibility.

The contractor should have clear and defined health and safety procedures, be actively training its employees in health and safety matters including general awareness, have a rigid safety management system in place and be able to support this with comprehensive records. The contractor should demonstrate a competent and pro-active approach to health and safety. Correct labelling and storage of chemicals and compliance with *The Control of Substances Hazardous to Health Regulations*[(1)] can provide some indication of the contractor's approach to safety.

One particular aspect of safe operating procedures is the use of permits-to-work. These provide a controlled system of work in hazardous or sensitive areas. They are issued to suitably trained personnel by an authorised person. Where they are in use, the client should be aware of and understand their purpose and function.

15.2.5 Technical proficiency

All plant on the asset register should be maintained in accordance with agreed schedules which identify the extent of the work and the frequency. The HVCA has produced standard maintenance schedules for many items of plant[(2)]. The results of maintenance inspections and follow-up work need to be supported by detailed records compiled by the contractor together with other relevant documentation.

In many instances, the contractor will be operating an approved quality assurance system which, in turn, will require documentation to demonstrate that work has been completed as stated.

Spares, replacement parts and materials will be required during maintenance activities. There will be cost, reliability and quality implications for these, possibly also related to standards of performance or manufacture.

It may be deemed necessary for the contractor to draw up a list of essential spares which are to be retained on site to ensure ready availability. There will be a cost associated with this task and the list should be agreed by the client.

The need for access to the building and its engineering services may require admittance of the contractor's personnel to controlled or secure areas. Adequate arrangements need to be in place and monitored. It may also be useful periodically to review who has access to plant areas and to ensure that, where necessary, arrangements exist for access out of normal hours.

Normal plant operation should include monitoring that systems are performing efficiently, particularly in terms of energy use. It may be a client requirement to include, as part of maintenance review meetings, a routine report on energy use and opportunities to improve efficiency, possibly including details of energy consumption and costs (see section 15.2.3).

Environmental aspects of maintenance and operation should also be addressed. All legislation should be complied with, good practice codes adopted where appropriate and all matters needing attention reported formally to the client.

15.2.6 Invoicing

Invoicing and payment procedures should be agreed between all parties at the start of the contract. They may include such matters as frequency of submission, payment terms, need for authorisation (e.g. for additional work) and expenditure limits (e.g. up to £200 value of essential work can be carried out without prior authorisation). An agreed format in which invoices are to be submitted should be established at the start of the agreement, although this may need to be reviewed as the contract progresses. The submitted invoices should be checked for accuracy and may be subject to a review procedure by the client's professional adviser, where appointed.

15.3 Scoring system

A simple, easily understood scoring system should be adopted at the start of the maintenance performance assessment process. A three-tier scoring system for the audit document shown in Appendix 15.A1 is proposed to provide an initial guide, see Table 15.1.

Table 15.1 Three-tier scoring system for maintenance performance

Assessed achievement	Score
Poor	1–3
Average	4–6
High	6–9

A five-tier scoring system would give greater scope for discrimination, provided that each performance category is adequately defined and understood fully.

It may be appropriate to apply different multipliers to each of the assessment headings to indicate their relative importance. For example, management might have a multiplier of 1.5, while invoicing could have a multiplier of 0.6. The multiplier is shown as the 'weighting factor' in the 'total score' section in Appendix 15.A1.

Table 15.2 Checklist for building documentation

Type of document
Fire certificate
Records of fire detection and alarm tests
Sprinkler system test records
Smoke extract system test records
Escape route pressurisation system test records
Electrical system safety inspection records
Electrical earthing and insulation test records
Portable appliance test records
Emergency lighting system test records
Fire extinguisher and fire hose reel test records (*BS 5306*[3])
Legionella risk assessment and routine inspection records
Notification of cooling towers and evaporative condensers
COSHH records
Lift insurance inspection reports
Lifting equipment insurance test reports and certificates
Pressure vessel and system test reports and certificates
Fume cupboard test reports and certificates
Operating and maintenance manuals
Waste disposal and handling procedures
Noise assessments
Asbestos awareness reports
General risk assessment
Gas safety inspection record

1.0	Introduction and overview of previous audit	
2.0	Agreed objectives and extent achieved	
3.0	Current audit assessments, trends and comments	
	3.1	Management
	3.2	Maintenance service
	3.3	Communication
	3.4	Health and safety
	3.5	Technical proficiency
	3.6	Invoicing
4.0	Overall review	
5.0	Concerns, future objectives and actions required	
6.0	Other related matters	
7.0	Date and time of next audit	

Figure 15.1 Sample outline agenda for maintenance audit meeting

The aggregate score can then be obtained by adding all the individual scores. While each individual audit may be difficult to analyse, noting trends in how the scoring changes over time will provide a useful indication of how standards are being maintained. Any deterioration on standards should be discussed fully at the following maintenance review meeting.

15.4 Recording comments

It is expected that comments will be produced during the audit, many of which may not need to be recorded. However, it will be useful for future reference to record anecdotal notes, special achievements or significant failings. Where scores of less than 3 or more than 7 are entered, they should be supported by explanatory comments.

15.5 Audit procedure

The audit procedure should consist of the following steps:

(*a*) determine the audit date and instruct contractor to attend

(*b*) arrange professional support if required

(*c*) complete audit form

(*d*) carry out inspections as required of plant rooms etc.

(*e*) carry out inspections of log sheets, reports, and supporting building documentation (see Table 15.2 for an indicative list)

(*f*) attend audit meeting or maintenance review meeting and discuss situation with contractor (see Figure 15.1 for an outline agenda)

(*g*) agree future action, including period until next audit

(*h*) prepare formal record of meeting

(*i*) monitor agreed action is being achieved.

References

1 *The Control of Substances Hazardous to Health Regulations 1999* Statutory Instrument 1999 No. 437 (London: The Stationery Office) (1999)

2 *Standard maintenance specification for mechanical services in buildings: Volume 1: Heating and pipework systems* HVCA **SMG90** (1990); *Volume 2: Ventilating and air conditioning* HVCA **SMG90b** (1991); *Volume 3: Control, energy and building management systems* HVCA **SMG90c** (1992); *Volume 4: Ancillaries, plumbing and sewerage* HVCA **SMG90d** (1992); *Volume 5: Electrics in buildings* HVCA **SMG90e** (London: Heating and Ventilating Contractors Association) (dates as indicated)

3 *BS 5306: Fire extinguisher installations and equipment on premises (7 parts)* (London: British Standards Institution) (various dates)

4 Nanayakkara R and Smith M H *Operation and maintenance audits* BSRIA Application Guide **AG24/97** (Bracknell: Building Services Research and Information Association) (1997)

Appendix 15.A1: Maintenance audit check sheet for building services

Client

Building

Location (address)

Contract type

Contract start date

Contractor

Assessor

Assessment date

Part 1 Management

1A Contractor's relationship with client (e.g. contract compliance, reports, meetings, contractor role, client support)

Score 1 2 3 4 5 6 7 8 9

Comments

1B Contractor's staff (e.g. quality of resource, resource management/supervision, conduct, housekeeping, work requests, emergencies, training)

Score 1 2 3 4 5 6 7 8 9

Comments

Part 2 Maintenance service (e.g. PPM, service provided, response time, positive approach, dealing with complaints, flexibility and innovation, effectiveness of planning, service level)

Score 1 2 3 4 5 6 7 8 9

Comments

Part 3 Communication (e.g. clarity, concerns with client, with occupants [where appropriate], quality of advice, responding to queries/complaints)

Score 1 2 3 4 5 6 7 8 9

Comments

Part 4 Health and safety (e.g. general awareness, knowledge of regulations, management, procedures, training, permits-to-work, records)

Score 1 2 3 4 5 6 7 8 9

Comments

Part 5 Technical proficiency (e.g. PPM performance, records and reports, quality assurance, materials and spares, security, energy efficiency, environmental matters)

Score 1 2 3 4 5 6 7 8 9

Comments

Part 6 Invoicing (e.g. procedure, format, accuracy, timescale)

Score 1 2 3 4 5 6 7 8 9

Comments

Continues

Total score

Item	*Score*		*Weighting factor*		*Total*
Part 1 Management: Client	_____	x	_____	=	_____
Staff	_____	x	_____	=	_____
Part 2 Maintenance service	_____	x	_____	=	_____
Part 3 Communication	_____	x	_____	=	_____
Part 4 Health and safety	_____	x	_____	=	_____
Part 5 Technical proficiency	_____	x	_____	=	_____
Part 6 Invoicing	_____	x	_____	=	_____
				Total	_____

16 Condition surveys

Contents

Summary

The application of condition surveys to various types of building services installations is described and the characteristics of different types of survey, ranging from a general overview to a thorough survey, are detailed.

The part that can be played by thermal imaging techniques is explained and the need for consistent presentation of information noted.

To improve the usefulness of the results of a survey to a client, the need for some form of prioritisation of actions is stressed and three categories are proposed.

Methods of data collection are described, ranging from simple, hand-written recording to sophisticated modern technology. The need for updating information is highlighted.

Condition appraisals, or condition surveys as they are more commonly called, can be defined as: 'the subjective assessment of the present condition of an individual component or complete system or installation,' or, 'the compilation of data referring to the state of repair of a building and its engineering services'.

A condition survey may be called for by a building occupier to provide comprehensive information on the current state of a building and its services or by a client considering the purchase or leasing of a building. In either case, a detailed brief should be agreed with the organisation carrying out the survey to ensure that particular requirements are met.

A client will undoubtedly expect his or her professional adviser on building services to provide clear and concise information on short- and long-term maintenance needs. When correctly undertaken, a condition survey not only gives this information but also provides a complete profile of the maintenance requirements for a building. Such a survey will allow an owner, or whoever is responsible for the repair and maintenance of the building, to decide what work should be done, when it should be carried out and the likely cost of the work to be undertaken.

If such exists, the building's Health and Safety File must be made available to the person carrying out a condition survey. Additional and valuable information is often obtained by monitoring plant and equipment in operation, and by reading log books, invoices, and servicing, operation and maintenance manuals or reports. Every effort should be made to seek out these documents because the information can be invaluable when making recommendations in the final survey report. Interviewing the servicing or maintenance contractor can also provide information not readily obtained from a purely subjective assessment.

In many instances, maintenance requirements are estimated from a visual inspection of the site. Even though the inspections may be undertaken annually, they can overlook long-term problems and fail to identify when items require replacement prior to failure. Encased or hidden services cannot be confidently assessed unless physically inspected. If a survey is to be non-invasive, all parties (client, contractor, surveyor etc.) need be aware that plant and services will *not* be dismantled or opened-up for internal inspection.

It is usual for a survey to be restricted, and for inaccessible areas of structures and finishes *not* to be opened-up for inspection. Where removable covers are accessible, however, these should be removed to inspect the services they encase. Invasive surveys, because of the disruption they can cause, are difficult to undertake in an occupied building and should not be contemplated without the client's full agreement.

Maintenance budgets often fall seriously short of what is required. In such cases accurate and meaningful information on the impact of the shortfall is important; it provides a basis for the consideration of remedial action, enables decisions to be made and allows a maintenance manager or building owner to allocate the budget sensibly over a range of activities. Where financial constraints are imposed, which is invariably the case, this method of working is often economically and professionally sound. However, inadequate investment may result in a particular problem never being resolved as year after year finance is allocated to keep pace with a problem rather than to resolve or eliminate it. In this situation, a condition survey is a useful management tool assisting the maintenance manager to:

— set priority objectives
— plan short-term expenditure
— justify longer-term investment.

16.1 Type and frequency

BS 8210[1] suggests that an in-depth survey is undertaken once every five years supplemented by a more superficial two-yearly inspection. This frequency can, of course, vary depending on the purpose for which the survey is required and the condition of the engineering services.

Where an effective regime of maintenance review meetings is operating (see section 15.2.3) it may be reasonable to relax the frequency of in-depth surveys. It would be necessary, however, to ensure that the routine reviews are predictive and do not simply respond to events as they occur.

Most professional services allow for choice and diversity. Engineering surveys are no exception, and there are several types of surveys available to suit the short- and long-term policies and objectives of most clients. Costs can vary significantly depending on the type of survey undertaken and the extent of detail of the report. It is widely recognised that an inspection, in whatever form it takes, provides an ideal starting point in assessing maintenance priorities. It is extremely important at the outset to establish the precise limits of the client's brief or the limitations of the survey to be undertaken. This will ensure that there is no misunderstanding as to the information to be included in the final survey report. The brief must identify why the report is required, what information is expected from the survey and how the information is to be presented and subsequently used. Photographs are a great help in highlighting specific issues of concern and can, if necessary, be used as an *aide-mémoire* at some later date.

Typical types of survey are indicated in the following sections.

16.1.1 Overview assessment

An overview assessment of the building services identifies immediate maintenance needs from observed data previously obtained from *ad hoc* visits and capitalises on the knowledge a surveyor may have of the site.

This type of survey will give clients a relatively accurate assessment of the financial commitment required in the forthcoming year but will be of limited accuracy for subsequent years. A physical inspection of the site would not normally be undertaken unless the individual surveyor wished to inspect a known problem area in more detail to be certain that the nature of the defect was fully understood. An overview assessment can only be undertaken by someone who knows the site. If the surveyor is not familiar with the site, he or she will need to carry out a physical inspection.

A schedule of repairs will be produced indicating the nature of the remedial works and their cost. If areas are identified as requiring attention beyond year one, the year in which the repairs should be undertaken will be indicated wherever possible. If a surveyor has been making *ad hoc* visits throughout the year, he or she should also have knowledge of any seasonal problems.

An energy report is not usually part of this type of survey.

16.1.2 Two-year maintenance plan

This is a physical overview assessment identifying the immediate maintenance needs and those required over the next two and, possibly, three years.

This level of survey, while being a distinct service, is something of a 'half-way house'; however, it does provide a client with reliable information and a clear indication of the state of repair of the building services. A physical inspection of the site would be made, noting expected repairs and the likely expenditure required during the next three years. An energy report is, again, usually excluded although obvious cases of excess energy consumption would need to be reported.

In addition to the schedule of repairs, a brief overview report would be prepared to give a medium-term strategy for maintenance.

16.1.3 Full condition survey

There is always the risk that overview inspections will miss the more serious but less obvious maintenance issues. While the cost may prohibit a full, in-depth survey on a frequent basis, an annual overview inspection supplemented by a more thorough survey once every five years does provide an ideal compromise. This approach will provide a client with a comprehensive assessment of maintenance needs for the short- and medium-term, that is 1–5 years. It should be noted, however, that for many businesses, or for long-term development reasons, clients may require a 10-year maintenance profile.

A full in-depth survey would generally contain the following information:

(*a*) an executive summary of the site covering the salient points emerging from the survey

(*b*) sub-reports relating to:

- external services
- incoming services
- mechanical services
- electrical services
- control systems
- achievement of performance parameters
- energy management and environmental assessment.

Each sub-report would include an investment summary for that particular element, identifying the maintenance and remedial requirements, their cost and the year in which the work should be undertaken. Graphical investment profiles can also be presented in an appendix, to illustrate a total and five-year investment sum (see section 13.9). This information provides accurate and useful information enabling a client to set priority objectives with confidence and plan both short- and long-term maintenance needs.

It is important to say that, from the client's point of view, the information will be incomplete if an engineering assessment is carried out in isolation. Without information on the building fabric, including the grounds and external works, the client will not be able to assess the total repair and maintenance requirement. It is also advisable that an energy and environmental assessment overview report is included. Only then will the complete maintenance picture unfold. This approach enables a comprehensive investment profile to be prepared and ensures that the works are complementary to each other and compatible in terms of timing when they are carried out.

It should be noted that risk assessment is a separate issue and falls outside the scope of a conventional condition survey. This must be pointed out to a client at an early stage because, if it is included, other professional experts may need to be engaged (see section 12). A condition survey or a maintenance plan will, however, if undertaken correctly, identify general health and safety issues together with all items of a repair and maintenance nature. The information collected will be of considerable help to a client in setting priority objectives and planning short-, medium- and long-term expenditure on maintenance works.

The surveyor should not only have the relevant experience but must also be capable of:

— surveying the site(s) within a reasonable time scale
— rapidly collecting and processing the maintenance data
— establishing or reviewing and revising a maintenance plan
— estimating the cost of the maintenance work required
— categorising data in a priority order
— creating a database for maintenance backlog.

16.1.4 Dilapidation reports

Most engineering surveyors will be familiar with dilapidation reports. Such reports are usually attached to a conventional condition survey. While the condition survey outlines the present condition of a building and its services, the dilapidation report takes into account the terms of the lease defining the responsibilities of the tenant and landlord for repair and maintenance and any building covenants. Schedules of dilapidations should be treated as a separate entity. If a schedule of dilapidation is prepared for a client at the end of a lease, it should identify any significant variations in the condition of the fabric and engineering services compared with their condition at the start of the lease. There would, therefore, be no need for a condition survey to be undertaken.

At the commencement of a lease, a dilapidation report should be prepared which identifies the condition of the fabric and services at that time. This can then be used as a bench mark in the future (for example when the building is vacated) to identify what, if any, deterioration or dilapidation has taken place. Photographs incorporated in the report, taken before the start of a lease, serve as a very useful *aide-mémoire* in the event of a dispute occurring.

16.2 Thermal imaging

There are certain highly sensitive and critical installations that may require more than a subjective visual assessment of their present condition. In such cases, the cost of thermal imaging may be justified compared with the consequential problems that could arise as a result of plant failure.

Thermal imaging is a technique for presenting a coloured representation of an elevation where different colours indicate the temperatures of the exposed surfaces. There is a distinct correlation between temperature and electrical resistance generated from faulty equipment, so any problems occurring due to faulty components, loose connections or corroded terminals will show up on the thermal image as 'hot spots'. Care must be taken, however, in interpreting the data. Conclusions formed should be based on trends rather than definitive temperatures because hot spots can result from inherent design irregularities and have nothing to do with loose terminals or corrosion.

Clearly, if the component under test involves live wires, it is essential that safe working practices are adhered to. Provided that adequate care is taken thermal imaging, being non-contact, is relatively safe to carry out because it relies on the amount of radiation emitted from the equipment being checked.

In recent years thermal imaging has become more widely used to assess the condition of electrical equipment in panels and similar items of plant. In addition it can be used to to highlight hot spots in mechanical services (due to poor bearings, deteriorated thermal insulations etc.) and to give a rapid assessment of shortcomings in the integrity of building fabric (inadequate or collapsed thermal insulation). The degree to which this is successful is primarily determined by the emissivity of the fabric surface and the ability of the camera to translate the information it receives into a pictorial image. Nevertheless, this technique is a powerful way of identifying heat loss or excessive loss due to badly installed or collapsed insulation without spending considerable time taking temperature readings.

As an alternative, single point surface temperature measurement devices are available but, while much cheaper to buy or hire, are unlikely to give the same level of results. It is also difficult to obtain consistent temperature readings from some surfaces.

16.3 Consistency of information

There is little doubt that individual buildings have their own particular maintenance requirements. These requirements will depend on:

— the performance criteria for the building
— the age and type of the building engineering services
— the design and specification of the building engineering services
— the maintenance history of the building services.

Where buildings on an estate are being considered by different surveyors (some major clients have hundreds of buildings), it is important to have a common and consistent recording and assessment system. It will be of enormous benefit if the surveyor has prior knowledge of the site and is therefore aware of the maintenance problems encountered over previous years. Even with such knowledge, however, the judgement of priorities may be out of step with that of other colleagues undertaking similar surveys on other buildings of the estate unless there is a standard classification system.

When the engineering survey is undertaken in conjunction with a building fabric survey, care must be taken to ensure there is consistency in data collection. Location, block and

Table 16.1 Classification of data from services condition survey

Condition	Designation	Explanation
1	Hazardous	Requires urgent attention Closure of building imminent Presents a danger if left unattended
2	Bad	While not dangerous must receive a high priority because of its bad state
3	Partly bad	Affected parts only should receive a high priority
4	Poor	While unsatisfactory, presents no immediate risk of failure. Replacement or repair should be considered in the near future
5	Reasonable	Satisfactory, operating as intended. Routine maintenance only required. Review at next opportunity
6	Good	As new and requires no remedial attention

room references have to be the same for each discipline if the data are to be meaningful. This will help to ensure all elements of the survey are ultimately carried out in a complementary way by focusing on an exact location within the management data file. Where duplicate plant or standby equipment is installed, it is important to establish not only its exact location but also the specific item to which the surveyor is referring in the report.

16.4 Classifying priorities

An organisation's building stock represents one of its most important assets and, generally, reflects many years of investment. This type of asset requires, and deserves, continuous care and protection. Despite this requirement, it is perhaps astonishing to find that the level of financial investment in the care and protection of buildings and their services often falls seriously short of what is required.

There is often a danger that, when resources are scarce, long-term investments are passed over for simpler and less expensive short-term measures.

It is clearly wise to look at maintenance in relation to other property running costs as it has to compete with other high-priority demands such as heating, lighting and cleaning. However, it can be argued that a cutback in maintenance expenditure causes difficulty in other areas; for example, increased expenditure on energy, reduced morale among building occupants and the failure of equipment which, in turn, could undermine the economic life of the plant. It is important, therefore, to spend a limited maintenance budget wisely. To help in this the following categories can be applied to help set priorities:

— Priority A (urgent): health and safety requirements, statutory duties and contractual obligations

— Priority B (necessary): minimising the deterioration of other services

— Priority C (desirable): environmental considerations.

Alternatively, a simple numerical coding obtained from a survey of the services can be used to set priorities, as outlined in Table 16.1. This table can be used in conjunction with the priority ratings given above. In addition, it is helpful to a client if the particular legislation which the maintenance defect contravenes is indicated within the survey report (for example, 'Electricity at Work Act 1989'). Failure to meet statutory requirements will feature highly in any survey and it is extremely important that the surveyor is up to date with the relevant current legislation.

It is important to realise that the terms 'condition' and 'priority' do not have the same meaning. Condition relates to the present state of the individual component or complete system while priority determines when the identified work requires to be undertaken.

16.5 Data collection

The availability of accurate and meaningful information is a fundamental requirement of any data collection system. There are three distinct ways of collecting site data:

— manual (paper) systems

— optical markers or readers

— computer systems.

16.5.1 Manual (paper) systems

This method of collection is by far the most common and will no doubt continue to be so for some time. This is in a large part attributable to the fact that while information technology (it) systems are numerous and readily available, they are generally misunderstood.

Low-technology manual systems are very suitable for many small to medium installations, and walking around a site with a *pro forma* data collection sheet is still popular with surveyors. In many instances the information collected is subsequently transferred to some form of computerised system for ease of amendment or updating. *Pro forma* data sheets help to minimise the possibility of inconsistent information or criteria where more than one surveyor is involved. However, the *pro forma* must be adequate for the purpose of the inspections to be carried out and the surveying team must receive adequate training on how to complete the form. When the survey is completed, large volumes of paper will probably need to be archived. As more surveys are undertaken, this volume can become unmanageable.

When these facts are considered, together with the problems of typing, checking and subsequent updating of manually collected data, the use of IT systems would appear to be a sensible solution. Initial set-up costs may be relatively high, but the long-term benefits are significant.

16.5.2 Electronic data collection

The development in computers has been significant in recent years and today many simple and relatively straightforward electronic data capture systems are available. Information gathered on site, obtained by answering pre-set questions, can easily be directly downloaded into a computer back in the office. Many of the computer systems incorporate bar-code readers which are ideal for creating an asset register and for tracking assets. This is not only suitable for plant and equipment but can be applied to portable appliance testing.

The systems available include:

— Optical mark readers: these have been available for many years. Using one of these, a surveyor can quickly carry out a survey using an optical mark reader pen to answer pre-set questions on a standard *pro forma* reporting form specially designed for the task in hand. The answers are scanned directly into the reader. One of the main drawbacks is that care must be taken to complete all the questions on the reporting form: failure to answer one question may cause the system to fail.

— Hand-held computers: these are robust, easy to carry around and relatively cheap. Their compact size generally means that they operate by a keypad using menu-driven software. The lack of a full QWERTY keyboard can, however, restrict their operation in terms of flexibility. Conversely, palm-top machines, while using a QWERTY keypad, are not as robust as hand-held machines.

— Tablet pen-based computers: these are now available from several manufacturers. Being light in weight they are easy to carry around a site and integrate easily with printers, bar code readers and scanners. The software is client-driven with the surveyor working from a list of user-defined standard specifications, descriptions, areas etc. Many of these systems can be used as a desktop computer and are compatible with standard software packages available today in most offices. The pen facility allows text to be hand written. Computer-aided design (CAD) modules can also be used as a peripheral tool allowing record drawings to be updated on site.

The main benefits of electronic data collection are:

— low capital cost

— flexibility and ease of operation

— little or no computer knowledge required to operate the base systems

— savings in administrative time

— information is accurate and consistent

— corrections can easily be made to the recorded data.

16.6 Updating information

This is an important task and must be done on an annual basis. If neglected the impetus of the initiative will be lost and the information previously collected will quickly become out of date.

16.7 Future developments

With a high proportion of both public and private sector buildings erected during the past 35–40 years, many experts in the maintenance sector have predicted that there will shortly be an eruption in maintenance requirements. Until the mid-1970s, prefabricated materials were used which, while giving speedy construction, paid little attention to future maintenance or running costs. Now, some 30 years later, many of these buildings and their engineering services require major attention to restore their condition to a reasonable state. All too often maintenance budgets fall short of what is required. The gap between the assessed need and financial provision is getting progressively wider. Provided that adequate finance is made available to undertake maintenance work, this predicted increase in maintenance can be avoided or, at least to some extent, cushioned.

References

1 *BS 8210:1986 Guide to building maintenance management* (London: British Standards Institution) (1986)

Bibliography

Condition based maintenance for building services BSRIA Technical Note **TN1/95** (Bracknell: Building Services Research and Information Association) (1995)

Maintenance of mechanical services Building Bulletin **70** (London: Department for Education and Employment/The Stationery Office) (1990)

Stock condition surveys RICS Guidance Note (London: Royal Institution of Chartered Surveyors (1997)

Box B *School condition surveys — a five year plan* Chartered Surveyor Monthly Series **1**(3) 6–7 (1991)

Legislation, non-compliance and condition appraisal systems BCIS Special Publication 249 (London: Building Cost Information Service) (1996)

Danny S S Whole-life property assessment management *Proceedings of the Construction Industry Board and Working Commission W70 on Maintenance and Modernisation* (Edinburgh: Department of Building, Heriot Watt University) (1988)

Maintenance and renewal in educational buildings: needs and priorities Design Note **40** (London: Department for Education and Employment/The Stationery Office) (1985)

Local house condition surveys Department of Environment Guidance Manual (London: The Stationery Office) (1993)

Holmes R *Property condition assessment — a cost effective approach* CIB Technical Information Service **TIS122** (Ascot: Chartered Institute of Building) (1990)

17 Health and safety

Contents

Summary

Various factors are identified which, to varying degrees, come within the sphere of operation and maintenance responsibility and can exert an influence on the health, safety and well-being of the occupants of a building.

The first is indoor air quality. The influence of this on both external and indoor factors is discussed and the monitoring of air quality explained, with some of the key contaminant influences described in some detail. Air quality standards relating to health and safety are outlined.

Thermal comfort influences are dealt with, and the relationship between activity rates, clothing levels and ambient conditions are described.

The need for air distribution systems to supply fresh or purified air to work places is recognised and for duct and system cleanliness noted. Assessment of the potential effects of refurbishment works on the well-being of occupants is examined with factors such as noise, airborne contaminants and ventilation considered. Assessment schedules for air quality, air distribution installations and thermal comfort are recommended and outlined.

The progressive introduction of regulations to support the *Health and Safety at Work etc. Act 1974*[1] has led to increasing awareness by management of factors affecting the health, safety and welfare of the workforce. As well as the requirement to consider health and safety in operational procedures, a healthy environment must be provided in the workplace. Prominent in these considerations is air quality. Management should bear in mind not only contaminants that may be created by working procedures but also pollutants from the ambient environment that may be drawn into the workplace by mechanical or natural ventilation. Additionally, the potential risks to the workforce of passive smoking is attracting increasing attention.

Thermal comfort requirements under statutory obligations are very modest but management needs to be aware that productivity can suffer when temperature extremes are encountered.

Specific regulations cover the matter of cleanliness in ventilation systems in addition to the need for a supply of wholesome air to the workplace. As well as meeting these requirements, it is prudent for management to keep some form of written record of the measures taken.

17.1 Indoor air quality

Air quality within a building is influenced by external and internal factors. The ability to maintain satisfactory air quality depends on identifying the factors that affect air quality in a particular application, controlling or eliminating detrimental factors and promoting beneficial ones.

External factors include:

- vehicle traffic, including parking facilities
- building geography, urban or rural
- neighbouring land use, industrial or commercial.

Internal factors can include:

- occupant related-effects, including smoking
- effects of furnishing equipment and building materials.

The primary methods of controlling air quality are:

- elimination: removing potential contaminants from the workplace
- substitution: replacing materials with less harmful alternatives
- dilution: the reduction in concentration of harmful contaminants through the introduction of less contaminated or uncontaminated air.

17.1.1 External factors

Ambient air pollution is generally caused by energy provisions for industry and by transport and its control in overall terms is, therefore, usually the responsibility of central or local government. External pollutants may be diluted by locating fresh air intakes away from pollutant sources. This normally involves siting ventilation air intakes at roof level, away from chimney flues, soil vents, standing water and cooling towers. Air ventilation intakes at ground floor level should be avoided wherever possible.

Where a ventilation air intake is unavoidably close to pollution sources, control measures should be implemented to remove or reduce contaminants to acceptable levels; CIBSE TM21 *Minimising pollution at air intakes*[2] gives detailed guidance.

17.1.2 Internal factors

The major sources of contaminants in the workplace are occupants, office furnishings and equipment. All may affect actual or perceived air quality. Occupants generate odours, skin flakes, bacteria and other bio-effluents. Office furnishings release solvent vapours including volatile organic compounds, such as formaldehyde, as does office equipment such as copiers which also release ozone.

All three primary methods of control are applicable to indoor pollution: eliminating contaminants by preventing the use of volatile solvents, substituting where possible with water-based paints, and diluting dust and odours through the introduction of fresh, filtered air.

Ventilation systems with terminal recirculatory facilities may act as secondary contaminant sources as internally generated dust and microbes will, unless removed by regular filter replacement and cleaning, accumulate and be ejected back into the workplace.

Guidance on indoor air quality is provided in CIBSE Guide A[3]. Assessment of indoor air quality relies on the experience of engineers, building managers and air quality consultants to determine whether satisfactory ventilation rates are maintained, occupancy levels are within guidelines and housekeeping practices are effective.

17.1.3 Air quality monitoring

External contaminants may be assessed through visual inspection of fresh air intakes and their proximity to pollution sources. Local pollution data can be obtained from local authority monitoring stations. Specific contaminant sources such as generator flues, car park facilities and cooling towers should be monitored to determine any effects on the quality of ventilation air intake.

Petroleum or other fossil fuel-derived combustion products are the most common cause of deteriorating external air quality. Any fraction of vehicle or generator fumes may be sampled by an air quality consultant to determine whether infringement of World Health Organization (WHO) or Health and Safety Executive (HSE) guidelines has occurred. However, these pollutants are likely to cause an odour nuisance within a building before any one chemical component reaches unacceptable levels.

Where dilution to undetectable levels is not possible because of the siting of fresh air intakes or the need to maintain minimum fresh air supply rates, gas phase or absorption filtration should be applied to remove noxious fumes. Carbon monoxide cannot be removed by activated carbon filters, but most other harmful gases can.

Indoor contaminants cannot be exhaustively monitored without incurring excessive costs due to the low concentrations encountered and the large number of contributory substances. It is usual to monitor surrogate contaminants and, because of their association with other potentially harmful contaminants, arrive at an indication of relative air quality. Results may then be compared with similar property findings and World Health Organization or HSE standards to determine what standards are reasonably achievable, bearing in mind the nature of work, occupancy levels and ventilation system capabilities.

The following paragraphs cover the typical contaminants assessed.

17.1.3.1 Respired carbon dioxide

Ventilation is largely supplied to dilute body odour which is influenced by occupancy levels and the metabolic activity rate of occupants: see section 1 of CIBSE Guide A1[3]. Respired CO_2 provides a useful indication of whether adequate fresh air is being supplied. Obviously, this can be determined only under normal occupancy conditions. Where occupancy levels are low, the room air volume itself may be sufficient to dilute respired CO_2. Under such conditions, monitoring may become an unreliable measure of odour dilution and more subjective methods may need to be employed. Analysis is normally carried out using colorimetric gas detection tubes or gas cells.

17.1.3.2 Airborne particles

Dust arises from human activity, deterioration of building and furnishing fabric, and work practices. Particles may be drawn in from the external environment by the ventilation system or generated in the workplace. The majority of dust is harmless to healthy adults although some particles may carry harmful chemicals arising from fuel combustion or pathogenic microorganisms shed by occupants. What proportion of dust presents a particular hazard cannot be readily determined. The total dust burden is measured, therefore, and assumptions made that the greater the dust burden, the poorer the air hygiene and the greater the likelihood that harmful contaminants are present. Analysis is normally carried out using a laser particle counter or by gravimetric (filtration) methods.

17.1.3.3 Noxious gases

Noxious gases may be introduced from outside the building through the ventilation system or generated within the workplace. Typical gases sampled for include ozone, formaldehyde, carbon monoxide, oxides of nitrogen and sulphur dioxide.

Volatile organic compounds are often sampled as part of detailed building investigations but, as they are unlikely to be present in significant concentrations, sampling to establish their presence and concentration can be expensive. Recognising that HSE standards are not likely to be breached in the indoor environment, and that no recognised indoor standards are available for these gases, sampling should be carried out only in exceptional cases. In most cases a visual inspection of a building should be sufficient to highlight any gaseous contaminant sources and to decide on means for controlling these.

Analysis of noxious gases is carried out using a variety of methods, normally involving a colour indication analysis tube or chemically impregnated paper. Infrared electronic detection systems are also available, but these often require regular calibration. Invariably the lower the detection limit required, the less portable and more costly the sampling device.

17.1.3.4 Microorganisms

Bacteria and fungi are always present in the indoor environment but, in most cases, not at levels to be significantly detrimental to healthy adults. Microorganism concentrations are largely a result of occupancy levels and served environment hygiene practices within the occupied environment. Temperature, humidity and fresh air ventilation rates affect their proliferation, and satisfactory control of these components should ensure that microbe levels are not detrimental to occupants.

Airborne microorganisms may be sampled by drawing air across a growth medium followed by laboratory incubation and analysis to allow enumeration and species identification.

17.1.4 Air quality standards

For the purpose of health, safety and welfare, exposure to any contaminant known to be detrimental to health or to cause a nuisance such that normal work activities cannot be pursued, should be eliminated so far as is reasonably practicable regardless of whether or not any air quality guideline has been breached. Exceptions to this are where exposure to pollutants is unavoidable because they form a normal part of work practices.

Within the UK, the HSE publishes occupational exposure standards and maximum exposure limits for harmful substances[4]. These should be consulted in the event that elimination is not possible to ensure that control measures meet the stated criteria. The WHO publishes air quality guidelines[5] based on observable health effects and includes a margin of protection for more sensitive individuals. These standards are recommended where it is not reasonable to expect exposure.

17.2 Thermal comfort influences

The amount of heat generated within buildings is higher now than in the past due to increases in occupant density and in the amount of electrical equipment and, especially, personal computers. Consequently, internal comfort conditions have become more difficult to achieve and control. Poor thermal control is largely responsible for the discomfort of occupants, both directly and through increased perception of poor air quality.

Comfort depends on occupant activity, clothing and ambient conditions including air temperature, air movement and radiant heat sources.

The aim of air conditioning is to control the thermal environment, largely through simple adjustments to air temperatures. The method by which air temperature is adjusted and the effect that this has on overall comfort control will depend on the form of air conditioning employed and its ability to provide a uniform thermal environment. Increased cooling demand may be met by increased cool air supply, which may lead to increased air movement and discomfort from draughts. Alternatively, the demand for greater heating may affect relative humidity resulting in detrimental physiological symptoms.

Heating, ventilation and air conditioning systems are designed and installed to meet predicted thermal loads and occupancy patterns for a particular building design. The ability of the system to maintain comfort is assessed at the commissioning stage by recording cooling and heating capacity and air volume flow rates during system regulating procedures. Air movement in the conditioned space may also be measured at this stage. Confirmation that design assumptions are adequate cannot be given until actual occupancy levels are realised and the full range of weather conditions experienced.

17.2.1 Pre-occupancy environmental monitoring

Time constraints often preclude a comprehensive thermal assessment of the building environment at the pre-occupancy stage: factors such as normal occupancy conditions, thermal load and weather conditions cannot be readily simulated to obtain the operational performance of a building throughout a complete annual cycle. Instead, commissioning and its resulting data have to be relied on at this stage and, for this reason, adequate time must be allowed for the commissioning process.

It must be assumed that any alterations to the intended use of the building will have taken due account of the original design capabilities of the structure and its engineering services.

17.2.2 Post-occupancy environmental monitoring

As part of routine maintenance, air temperature and relative humidity will be monitored, through either a building management system (bms) or manual measurements. However, this does not take into consideration the effects of air movement, radiant heat sources and personal preferences.

The two primary means of determining whether satisfactory comfort is maintained are physical monitoring and personal evaluation by trained maintenance personnel, independent consultants and building occupants. A comprehensive assessment can be carried out in accordance with *ANSI/ASHRAE Standard 55-1992*[6] or equivalent. Where comfort control has been brought into question, experience, observations and communication with occupants to establish their views are all that is necessary to carry out a preliminary assessment.

The factors that affect comfort and the effectiveness of the air conditioning systems, together with the way they interact and how they can be manipulated, must be understood before any meaningful assessment of post-occupancy environmental monitoring can be carried out.

17.3 Air distribution systems

Air handling units should be operated in accordance with *The Workplace (Health, Safety and Welfare) Regulations 1992*[7], pursuant to the provision of a suitable volume of fresh or purified air. This requires that the highest standards of filtration be applied and that ongoing maintenance be based on reasonably practicable planned preventive measures, including hygiene.

Air handling units must be routinely inspected to ensure that deteriorating components, such as spent filters, are replaced as necessary and that other conditions likely to affect air quality — for example, water pooling within condensate drain trays or carry-over water on duct surfaces — are prevented or controlled. Minimum standards of cleanliness should be applied based on visual inspection and scheduled maintenance periods.

As standards of cleanliness are partly subjective, some components should be cleaned as a matter of routine. These components include air-intake equipment prior to filtration, post-filter chambers, condensate trays, cooling coils during the cooling period and humidification equipment during the heating period.

Filter condition provides the most convenient indicator of other condition-related maintenance requirements, and full cleaning of all air handling unit components should be undertaken at least once a year to return these to optimum hygienic condition.

Risk assessments should be prepared for each air handling unit to identify specific maintenance requirements and to confirm that adequate air filtration is applied, as determined by minimum filter standards and air source evaluation.

The effectiveness of ongoing maintenance should be periodically assessed and validated independently to confirm that satisfactory standards are being achieved. Annual inspection of air handling units is recommended, although representative units may be examined more frequently and their condition taken as indicative of similar systems.

Independent assessment is, to some extent, subjective, which is why attempts have been made to examine cleanliness based on the mass of dust and dirt deposition over a given surface area. One problem with this is that dirt often accumulates unevenly so that sampling from different areas will give different impressions of the cleanliness of a system. With this in mind, and assuming no other interests, an independent visual inspection is recommended. Representative photographs may be provided to assist in an objective evaluation of report findings.

17.3.1 Air distribution ductwork

New ductwork needs to be stored and installed in accordance with current standards of good practice, particularly to ensure the prevention of contamination. Independent inspections should be undertaken during installation and at the final inspection for deficiencies and defects; see also HVCA DW/TM2[8]. At the time of installation, adequate access should be provided to facilitate inspection of sensors and fire curtains, and to monitor cleanliness.

The handover of clean ductwork and high standards of ongoing maintenance should limit subsequent contamination of duct surfaces. Air handling equipment should be assessed at least once a year to provide an accurate indication of cleanliness. Representative areas of ductwork may then be examined on a five-yearly basis. Where distribution systems are extensive, separate areas may be examined more frequently, providing an indication of the condition of similar duct runs; see also HVCA TR/17 *Guide to good practice; cleanliness of ventilation systems*[9].

The cleanliness of supply ductwork systems is more serious than that of extract duct systems because of its more direct association with occupants; nevertheless, extract duct systems should be kept under review especially where air recirculation is operated.

Distribution ductwork systems with an unknown or questionable maintenance history may be affected by more significant contamination. More importantly, ducts or plenums may be of an age where the materials contain asbestos and are now deteriorating. The passage of supply air across damaged or unsealed asbestos tiles presents an unacceptable hazard.

For most applications, the ratio of air volume flow rate to the exposed internal surface area of the duct makes it unlikely that HSE exposure limits for airborne asbestos fibres[4] will be exceeded. However, an avoidable hazard remains and a failure to take reasonable control measures is likely to be poorly received by building occupants.

An asbestos register should clearly identify all asbestos materials. Damaged surfaces in contact with air should be replaced with non-asbestos alternatives as soon as practicable. All other asbestos should be sealed with a view to removal at the earliest practicable opportunity. Airborne fibre sampling should be carried out at supply diffusers to confirm compliance with current standards.

Other distribution network contaminants with no specific hazardous components should be assessed as to their likelihood of affecting air quality and the health and wellbeing of occupants of the conditioned space. Typical contaminants comprise a mix of organic and inorganic debris including vehicle-derived combustion products, vegetation, silica dust and recirculated dust such as skin flakes, paper and textile fibres. The effect of this contaminant mix is unknown although likely to contribute to at least superficial infection; it should, therefore, be prevented from accumulating to any significant degree.

Standards of cleanliness have been adopted by trade associations representing those involved in duct cleaning in an attempt to regulate the industry. It is advisable that specialist consultants who have no direct involvement with the physical cleaning of ductwork within the building are made responsible for determining the appropriate level of cleanliness for a particular situation. Illustrative photographs of existing conditions can help to provide an objective assessment of the initial state of the ductwork.

17.4 Modifications to existing buildings

An assessment of any major modifications and refurbishment should be undertaken to determine the effect on building occupants and maintenance staff. The headings below are indicative of the areas that should be addressed.

17.4.1 Noise nuisance

Can normal office work continue without interruption? If not, what precautions are necessary? Consider the following options:

(*a*) out of hours working

(*b*) acoustic barriers

(*c*) relocation of local office staff for the duration of work

(*d*) ear defenders for maintenance staff.

Monitor noise levels during the works and record sound pressure levels to confirm that preconstruction assumptions were correct. If noise levels exceed the control limits, review precautions and modify as necessary.

17.4.2 Airborne contaminants

Which of the following contaminants are likely to be released into the air?

(*a*) particulates

(*b*) fibres

(*c*) gases and vapours

(*d*) microbes.

What concentrations are likely to arise? Who will be affected? What precautions are necessary to protect health, safety and welfare?

17.4.3 Personal protective equipment

Assess the type of protection necessary to prevent nuisance or adverse health effects. Office modifications are likely to generate dust which may constitute a nuisance to maintenance staff and building occupants in the locality of the works; additionally, some of the dust released may contain recognised hazardous materials (e.g. glass fibre or asbestos). Any activity generating dust will require the protection of maintenance staff, office occupants and equipment, including ventilation systems.

Dust, in itself, may cause irritation while associated microorganisms may be released in high concentrations, particularly during the renovation of old structures. Vapour migration from construction materials may occur during the works and for some time after the work is completed. Adhesives used in construction will have been assessed as safe for use although most will specify the need for ventilation to control concentrations and dilute odours. Precautions should be taken to protect construction workers and building occupants from inhalation, ingestion and skin contact with potentially hazardous materials. Protective measures can include ori-nasal masks, gloves and dilution by supply air ventilation or local exhaust ventilation.

Enclosures should be erected around the work area, or at access routes, to contain contaminants. Coveralls, eye and respiratory protection should be provided as necessary for anyone working within the enclosure. Gloves should be supplied to prevent skin irritation, particularly for eczema sufferers.

Monitor contaminant levels within and local to the enclosure to confirm effective control. If control levels are exceeded, modify precautions.

17.4.4 Ventilation

Ventilation systems offer a means of controlling contaminants, including collection and removal. Measures should be taken to ensure that adequate fresh or purified air is provided to dilute generated contaminants. Recirculating systems should be isolated within the work zone to prevent distribution of contaminants to other occupied building areas. Extract diffusers should be taped shut and terminal recirculatory systems isolated unless required for ventilation and comfort control. Terminal equipment should be examined before starting the works and after completion to assess the need for filter replacement and unit cleaning.

Where extract ventilation has been isolated, local exhaust ventilation may be required to prevent pressurisation of the work area. Exhaust ventilation will also help consequent contaminant dilution. Contaminants should not be exhausted into the atmosphere without an assessment of the discharge point to confirm that it is safe to do so. Treatment (filtration) of the exhaust may be necessary depending on property boundaries, the discharge point and height, and the prevailing wind direction. See also CIBSE TM21 *Minimising pollution at air intakes*[2].

17.4.5 Who is to carry out safety assessments?

For the majority of refurbishments and modifications, familiarity with the hazards through day-to-day experience should be sufficient to identify the effect of work on the building environment and occupants and to recommend the appropriate control measures and precautions. Monitoring the effectiveness of precautionary measures may require the assistance of an expert such as an occupational hygienist or air quality consultant to provide independent assurance that the health, safety and welfare of occupants is protected.

17.4.6 Notification and record keeping

Notification of construction work should be made in writing to building and office managers. Records of the safety assessments, together with noise and air quality analysis results, should be kept within an on-site building log identifying assumptions made and precautions implemented.

17.5 Recommended assessment schedules

17.5.1 Air quality monitoring

Initial assessments are recommended at handover, prior to occupation, to confirm that satisfactory standards of air quality have been achieved and that system ventilation operation is unlikely to be detrimental to the health of occupants.

Ongoing assessments are carried out under normal occupancy conditions and should be carried out within one year of handover to confirm that satisfactory office and air distribution system hygiene standards are being maintained.

Routine monitoring should be carried out at the building facilities manager's discretion and on the basis of initial assessments. It is recommended that air quality indicators are routinely reviewed to assess seasonal variations, confirm the validity of initial assessments and demonstrate a commitment to the maintenance of satisfactory working conditions. Reviews of air quality may be carried out quarterly together with assessments of the air distribution system and thermal comfort. The actual frequency will be a balance between building size, age and budget constraints.

17.5.2 Air distribution system

Initial assessments are recommended during installation works to confirm that ductwork and equipment is delivered to site in a satisfactory condition of cleanliness and that storage arrangements minimise the entry of dust and contaminants. Installation proposals should be reviewed to confirm that adequate access has been allowed to facilitate maintenance and inspection. An intermediate inspection may be carried out at first fit and a final inspection as part of defect and deficiency inspections.

Ongoing assessments are recommended on an annual basis to validate the efficacy of planned preventive maintenance. The actual frequency of assessment should be based on the number of air handling units using, say, a three-monthly inspection while ensuring that each unit is inspected annually.

See also *Guide to good practice; cleanliness of ventilation systems* HVCA TR/17[9].

17.5.3 Thermal comfort

Initial assessment cannot determine the effect of occupants and equipment until normal occupancy conditions are realised. Likewise, the effect of solar gain and weather conditions cannot be assessed by carrying out a one-off spot check. Instead, commissioning data must be relied on.

Once the building is occupied, building maintenance personnel should record air temperatures and relative humidity levels as part of ongoing routine assessments. Occupants' comments as to satisfaction with working conditions should be monitored where appropriate and compared with BMS data and manual temperature readings to ascertain the likely cause of any complaints.

Periodic independent assessment is recommended to validate routine monitoring. Where dissatisfaction cannot be readily attributed to monitored conditions, assessment of the thermal environment should be undertaken. This should include a visual assessment of the workspace, together with measurement of air speed, draught, radiant heat gain, air temperature and humidity. Where occupant complaints are concentrated within one section or department it may be appropriate to review the relevant work practices and management techniques.

Routine monitoring at an appropriate frequency should be carried out to confirm satisfactory sensor calibration. Independent validation of control sensor settings may be carried out to identify discrepancies. Special investigations should be carried out in response to an exceptional level of complaints (e.g. in excess of 15–20% of occupants).

17.5.4 Modifications to existing buildings

Initial assessments should be carried out local to the construction enclosure to determine the air quality prior to the commencement of work. Where routine monitoring is an existing part of control strategies, data will already be available.

Ongoing assessments should be carried out at the earliest period during renovation work to determine the effectiveness of preventive measures and confirm the maintenance of satisfactory air quality throughout the remainder of the workplace.

References

1 *Health and Safety at Work etc. Act 1974* (London: Stationery Office) (1974)

2 *Minimising pollution at air intakes* CIBSE Technical Memoranda **TM21** (London: Chartered Institution of Building Services Engineers) (1999)

3 *Environmental criteria for design* in CIBSE Guide A1: Environmental Design (London: Chartered Institution of Building Services Engineers) (1999)

4 *Occupational exposure limits* HSE **EH40** (Sudbury: Health and Safety Executive) (revised annually)

5 *Air quality guidelines for Europe* (Copenhagen: World Health Organization) (1987)

6 *ANSI/ASHRAE Standard 55-1992 Thermal environmental conditions for human occupancy* (Atlanta GA: American Society of Heating, Refrigeration and Air Conditioning Engineers) (1992)

7 *The Workplace (Health, Safety and Welfare) Regulations 1992* (London: The Stationery Office) (1992)

8 *Guide to good practice; internal cleanliness of new ductwork installations* HVCA **DW/TM2** (London: Heating and Ventilating Contractors Association) (1991)

9 *Guide to good practice; cleanliness of ventilation systems* HVCA Technical Report **TR17** (London: Heating and Ventilating Contractors Association) (1998)

Bibliography

Workplace health, safety and welfare: The Workplace (Health, Safety and Welfare) Regulations 1992 Approved code of practice and guidance HSE **L24** (London: Health and Safety Executive) (1992)

Management of health and safety at work: The Management of Health and Safety at Work Regulations 1992 Approved code of practice (London: Health and Safety Executive) (1992)

How to deal with sick building syndrome HSE HS(G)132 (London: Health and Safety Executive) (1995)

Ventilation of the workplace HSE **EH22** (London: Health and Safety Executive) (1988)

Harrington J M and Gill F S *Occupational health: evaluating workplace hazards* (Oxford: Blackwell Science Publications) (1992)

The Control of Substances Hazardous to Health Regulations 1999 Statutory Instrument 1999 No. 437 (London: The Stationery Office) (1999)

The Control of Asbestos at Work Regulations 1987 Statutory Instrument 1987 No. 2115 (London: The Stationery Office) (1987)

Environmental design CIBSE Guide A (London: Chartered Institution of Building Services Engineers) (1999)

Installation and equipment data CIBSE Guide B (London: Chartered Institution of Building Services Engineers) (1986)

Loyd S R *Guidance and the standard specification for ventilation hygiene* BSRIA Facilities Management Specification **FMS1** (Bracknell: Building Services Research and Information Association) (1997)

Indoor air pollution — an introduction for health professionals US EPA publication 402R94007 (Washington DC: United States Environmental Protection Agency) (1994)

The work environment (vol. 3): indoor health hazards (London: Lewis Publishers) (1994)

Health, safety and welfare in the built environment CIBSE Technical Memoranda **TM20** (London: Chartered Institution of Building Services Engineers) (1995)

BS EN ISO 14001: 1996: Environmental management systems. Specification with guidance for use (London: British Standards Institution) (1996)

BS EN ISO 14005: Environmental assessment of sites and entities (London: British Standards Institution) (in preparation)

BS ISO 14004: 1996: Environmental management systems. General guidelines on principles, systems and supporting techniques (London: British Standards Institution) (1996)

BS EN ISO 14010: 1996: Guidelines for environmental auditing. General principles (London: British Standards Institution) (1996)

18 The Construction (Design and Management) Regulations

Contents

Summary

It is noted that maintenance comes within the definition of construction work under the *The Construction (Design and Management) Regulations 1994* and a brief résumé is provided of the requirements of these Regulations and the duties on various parties.

Particular reference is made to the provision of plant space for building services installations and the application of the Regulations to large-scale maintenance work is discussed. Requirements for handover documentation are listed.

Some details on the Health and Safety File are provided together with a hypothetical example of a hazard summary sheet.

The Construction (Design and Management) Regulations 1994(1), often referred to as the CDM Regulations, have numerous effects on maintenance work, particularly for building services.

Maintenance comes within the definition of 'construction work' set down in the Regulations. This means that all the requirements of the CDM Regulations apply to maintenance work. Although maintenance work has always been covered by the *Health and Safety at Work etc. Act 1974*(2), the CDM Regulations impose specific obligations and duties.

The CDM Regulations and the *Health and Safety at Work etc. Act* do not demand safety at any cost but they do require that work is made safe 'so far as is reasonably practicable'. This may not be understood clearly in some instances. In terms of making a maintenance task safe for the operative, 'reasonable practicability' entails a comparative assessment. The cost in money, time and resources of making an operative's task safer have to be weighed against the costs likely to be incurred if the operative suffers an injury.

The following sections offer a brief summary of the requirements of the CDM Regulations of primary relevance to maintenance. For greater detail on the duties and general requirements, the Health and Safety Executive approved code of practice(3) should be consulted.

18.1 Design risk assessments

To meet the requirements of the CDM Regulations, a designer must be competent and have the relevant skills and necessary resources, including technical facilities. A person designing an installation or piece of equipment which requires maintenance has a duty to carry out a risk assessment that includes the maintenance function. Where this assessment shows a hazard to the maintenance operative, the designer must reconsider the proposals and try to remove entirely, or to reduce and control, the risk. (The same requirements apply to risks to personnel installing the plant.)

18.2 Risk assessment of work routines

The term 'designer' has a broad interpretation under the CDM Regulations (see HSE Construction Information Sheet 41(4)) and includes individuals who prepare specifications, bills of quantities etc. Because of this, a person preparing detailed instructions for routine maintenance work is also classified as a designer and, hence, has a similar duty to evaluate the risks entailed in the work routines and attempt to eliminate or reduce them.

18.3 Plant space requirements

Building service designers have, traditionally, been put under pressure to keep plant space requirements to an absolute minimum thereby maximising the area of the building available for the occupier's use. This is probably because building services tend to be regarded as not making a tangible contribution to the objectives of the businesses that they serve. However, clients also have duties under the CDM Regulations and can no longer ignore the issue of safe maintenance practices. This should lead to a more reasonable general attitude to plant space requirements and consequent improvements in accessibility for maintenance.

18.4 Maintenance contracts

The application of the CDM Regulations to a project is dependent on the scale of the construction work (the definition of which includes maintenance).

It is not considered necessary for the HSE to be notified or a planning supervisor to be appointed for a maintenance contract *per se*, even for a large contract (of an aggregate duration of more than 500 person days over the term of the contract, or more than five people working at any one time, as indicated in the CDM Regulations). It would, however, be within the terms and definitions of the Regulations if the HSE were to require this. A more likely situation would be where a single maintenance task (e.g. a large boiler overhaul) falls within the notifiable project scale. In this instance, it would be fully appropriate for the Regulations to be applied and for a planning supervisor to be appointed.

Unaccompanied working features prominently in maintenance functions. While this is not referred to specifically in the CDM Regulations, they are clearly concerned with making maintenance work safer. There is always the possibility that a sole operative could be incapacitated while working in an 'authorised persons only' area and remain undetected for some time. To require accompanied working in all instances would add dramatically to maintenance costs and would, therefore, probably not be 'reasonably practicable'. It would, however, be fully practicable to arrange some form of call-up procedure for unaccompanied maintenance operatives and this should be considered carefully. (Any consistent infringement of this procedure by the operative would be likely to exonerate an employer in the event of an accident.)

18.5 Handover documentation

The majority of the information passed to the client by the designer at handover will form part of the Health and Safety File as required by the CDM Regulations and will consist of a wide variety of documents and drawings. Specific elements may include the following:

- operation and maintenance manual(s) for building services
- record drawings, plans and specifications
- general details of the construction methods and the materials used
- details of maintenance requirements and facilities
- details of known hazards and other health and safety information
- details of the location and nature of the utilities and services, including emergency and fire fighting systems
- test certificates for electrical and mechanical systems
- examination reports
- commissioning information
- contractual documentation
- equipment and material warranties
- record of all documents, including details of spares, keys etc.

18.6 Views of operatives

Part of the contractor's duties under the CDM Regulations is to make provision for the operatives' views and opinions on health and safety to be discussed and assessed. Again, there is no direct requirement for a maintenance contract that does not fall within the 'notifiable project' definition. However, it is worthwhile and reasonable to canvass the opinions of those with first-hand knowledge and experience of relevant tasks and to react to these views as appropriate.

18.7 Health and Safety File

The Health and Safety File is a document that is continuously developed throughout the design and construction of a building project. It comprises a structured collection of all the data about the building and its services relevant to health and safety.

Under the CDM Regulations, the building occupier has a statutory duty to ensure that the Health and Safety File is not only kept securely but is also readily available for inspection by any person who may need access to the information it contains. It is important, therefore, that the building occupier considers how the File will be indexed and maintained as well as appointing responsibility for implementing revisions. Working copies should be made of all important documentation so that originals (including a copy of the operating and maintenance manual) can be kept in a safe location, preferably on site.

The key item in the File is a summary of the significant hazards and risks inherent in the building and its services. It is essential that such a summary is confined to the salient risks and is not packed with details of normal, routine hazards, which would detract from its usefulness and effectiveness by masking major hazards. For most buildings, an effective hazard summary should comprise little more than a single page (see Figure 18.1). HSE Construction Information Sheet 41[4], which provides guidance on the role of the designer in providing information on health and safety, includes a very apt phrase which expresses the essence of the Health and Safety File generally and the hazard summary in particular: 'information needs to be included...*to alert others to risks which they cannot reasonably be expected to know*'. This guidance is applicable not only to designers but to all parties with an input to the Health and Safety File.

The design team would contribute initially to the File, followed by input from the construction or installation team; finally, when the building is in use, the facilities management team would add to the File, as appropriate. It is essential that the File remains 'alive' and is never considered to be completed or finalised.

In addition to all relevant health and safety information, the File should include other material that will assist in the operational use of the building such as:

(*a*) 'as installed' drawings, schematic diagrams, wiring diagrams, etc. together with relevant details of construction methods and materials used

(*b*) operation and maintenance instruction manuals including manufacturer's instructions for plant and equipment installed and details of maintenance

HAZARD SUMMARY

Site Albert Road, Borchester
Building No. 4 Administrative Offices

The following schedule provides a brief summary of significant risks that may not be readily apparent to personnel working on the above site/building. Personnel referring to the schedule must note that common hazards (e.g. medium voltage electricity, working at heights, handling materials marked clearly as hazardous) are excluded from the schedule as working procedures in these situations comprise part of standard operative training for normal levels of competence.

The source in the Health and Safety File for further information on the particular stated hazard is given in the right-hand column.

HAZARD	FURTHER INFORMATION
1 Hidden features	
a High voltage cabling in bulkhead builder's work duct in basement	Electrical services layout drawing nos. E758 – 28 and 29
b Soil contamination in delivery bay area	Site plan and specialist survey and report
c Wiring drops in demountable partitions serving light switches and socket outlets	Typical details in electrical services drawing no E758-64
d Legionellosis risk (Legionnaires' disease)	O&M manual, section M17 for precautions for operatives
2 Particular design features	
a Structural members not to be drilled or used for fixings	Structural schedule ref. S758-131
b Toxic materials; water treatment chemicals	O&M manual, section M17 for COSHH details and handling instructions
c Cleaning of atrium glazing	O&M manual, section A7 for procedures and instructions
d Demountable lifting beams in basement plant rooms B18 and B23	O&M manual, section M12 for instructions
e Refrigerant for water chiller in basement plant room B18	O&M manual, section M12 for Refrigeration Handling instructions
3 Control features	
a Isolation provisions for utilities and building services	Site plan for location and O&M manual for instructions as below:
i HV electrics	Section E1
ii MV electrical distribution; lighting small power and landlord's services	Section E1
iii Water main and distribution	Section M1
iv Gas main and distribution	Section M3
v Steam and LTHW distribution	Section M2
vi Chilled water and condenser cooling water.	Section M4
4 Emergency features	
a Escape routes	Floor layout plans A758-3 to A758-10 for details
b Fire alarm system	O&M manual, section E28 for details
c Fire protection systems	O&M manual, sections M8 for staircase pressurisation system and M14 for hose reel dry riser and sprinkler systems

Figure 18.1 Example of a hazard summary

requirements and facilities

(*c*) details of the location of public utilities and other services provided for the building

(*d*) test certificates, commissioning records, contractual documentation and proprietary equipment and material warranties.

Standards for the initial production of the File as part of the project should be set by the client under guidance from the planning supervisor. Such standards would cover format and presentation as well as content. The responsibility for maintenance of the File and assuring its ready availability to those who may require access to it after handover rests with the building occupier. It is important for the occupier's facilities manager to ensure that operational experience is added to the File content as appropriate. Similarly, the health and safety effects of any changes in legislation or technology should be incorporated.

BSRIA applications guide AG7/97[5] provides an excellent source of advice and guidance on the structure and content of the Health and Safety File, including a standard specification which may be used in procurement.

References

1 *The Construction (Design and Management) Regulations 1994* Statutory Instrument 1994 No. 3140 (London: Stationery Office) (1994)

2 *Health and Safety at Work etc. Act 1974* (London: The Stationery Office) (1974)

3 *Managing construction for health and safety: Construction (Design and Management) Regulations 1994 Approved code of practice* HSE **L54** (London: Health and Safety Executive) (1995)

4 *Construction (Design and Management) Regulations 1994: The role of the designer* HSE Construction Information Sheet **41** (London: Health and Safety Executive) (1995)

5 Nanayakkara R *The CDM Regulations health and safety file* BSRIA Applications Guide **AG7/97** (Bracknell: Building Services Research and Information Association) (1997)

Bibliography

Designing for health and safety in construction (London: Health and Safety Executive) (1995)

A guide to managing health and safety in construction (London: Health and Safety Executive) (1995)

Manual handling: guidance on regulations **HSE L23** (London: Health and Safety Executive) (1992)

Nanayakkara R *Standard specifications for the CDM Regulations health and safety file* BSRIA Application Guide **AG9/97** (Bracknell: Building Services Research and Information Association) (1997)

CDM Regulations — case study guidance for designers: an interim report CIRIA Report **145** (London: Construction Industry Research and Information Association) (1995)

CDM regulations — work sector guidance for designers CIRIA Report **166** (London: Construction Industry Research and Information Association) (1997)

Experiences of CDM CIRIA Report **171** (London: Construction Industry Research and Information Association) (1997)

CDM Regulations — practical guidance for clients and client's agents CIRIA Report **172** (London: Construction Industry Research and Information Association) (1998)

CDM Regulations — practical guidance for planning supervisors CIRIA Report **173** (London: Construction Industry Research and Information Association) (1998)

19 Training

Contents

Summary

An organisation's personnel are recognised to be its greatest asset and the training of staff needs to be planned and managed. The achievement and demonstration of individual and corporate competency is discussed together with the need to have a formal training policy.

Reference is made to the importance of identifying particular training requirements and more general training needs such as coverage of health, safety and quality management. An organisational plan and a dedicated budget are proposed for the training activity.

Means of providing training are highlighted and the importance of a suitable training environment is identified.

The need to 'confirm' training by some form of certification in order to evaluate the results and to keep records of training individual personnel is identified.

The greatest asset of any organisation is its employees and developing their skills is a sensible investment. Employees need to replace or refresh existing skills throughout their careers in order to maintain their market value. In turn, well trained and committed staff are better able to contribute to the future success of the organisation.

Training is a management tool that enables a company to attract and select the best qualified personnel and to retain them. A prospective employer which is able to demonstrate clear career opportunities and objectives, and which promotes development training, will always be in demand.

A commitment to training is essential to the success of an organisation. Training is gradually becoming a strategic priority in the management and future development of businesses. Training is a long-term investment, but an area that has traditionally suffered from cost-cutting in many organisations seeking higher levels of profit. Unreserved commitment from senior management is essential to developing a culture where training is properly valued throughout an organisation.

19.1 Management

The organisation of training cannot be left to chance; lack of consistency of purpose will result in failure.

Organisations should begin by identifying the most important operational requirements or problems to highlight training needs. They must then plan and initiate the training, which may be from in-house resources or by a specialist training provider. The selection of an outside specialist may require a small-scale trial to assess the suitability, effectiveness and cost. Once a satisfactory source or method has been identified, the training should be implemented. There is then an ongoing role in evaluating the effectiveness of the training. The cycle is one of learning and ongoing improvement. What forms of training do and do not work for that organisation are learnt systematically.

Emphasis on short-term profits must be countered by demonstrating the effectiveness of training and the benefits to the organisation.

19.2 Competency

Within the building services industry there is an increasing requirement for designers, engineers, technicians and tradesmen to be able to demonstrate and prove competence — this requirement is included within *The Construction (Design and Management) Regulations 1994*[(1)], for example. It is particularly important that those involved in an operation or process that is inherently hazardous are competent to perform the tasks required safely. Employers have a responsibility to do all that is reasonable and practicable to ensure that correct and appropriate training is provided.

The Management of Health and Safety at Work Regulations[(2)] define a competent person as 'a person who has sufficient training and experience or knowledge and other qualities'. The dictionary states that 'competence' is a state that includes being competent, suitableness, ability, sufficiency, legal capacity, legal right or authority.

Proof of competence is enshrined in health and safety legislation and much of that legislation applies to the building services industry. The need to demonstrate or prove competency applies as much to the designer and engineer as it does to the technician and tradesman. Training at every level should be focused, organised and delivered to meet that requirement.

19.3 Training policy statement

The organisation (internal or external) charged with the responsibility for operating and maintaining a modern building needs to identify a training policy which provides a clear statement of what it is seeking to achieve by way of development and training. The policy statement should identify the technical, health, safety, quality and performance standards relevant to the operation and maintenance function.

The aims of the strategy should be to:

- support and develop the business aims of the company
- identify the resources for training
- identify the benefits that will result from training
- enable managers and staff to contribute towards the achievement of business targets.

The training strategy should also set out key business targets and communicate these to staff, including the:

- importance of training within the company
- relationship between training needs and training
- importance of personal commitment to self-development.

19.4 Identification of training needs

19.4.1 Training needs and the building

To achieve the working or living environment, modern buildings utilise building engineering services to control that environment within appropriate limits. The modern building contains an increasing amount of advanced technology that controls not only the working environment but also the business processes carried out within the building. Those responsible for operating and maintaining the building need to acquire and develop the appropriate technical and managerial competency.

In order that a modern building can be managed successfully, all the factors that contributed to the original decision to construct the building have to be understood:

- building design concept
- method of construction
- building services
- financial objectives
- facilities management
- environmental and social issues
- core business process.

The skills and knowledge required to manage, operate and maintain the building services economically and effectively must be identified and suitable resources applied to carrying out that function.

The information contained within the operating and maintenance manuals, the record drawings, the commissioning records and the Health and Safety File, together with all the above, provide a comprehensive picture of the building. This set of data can then be used to develop the skills analyses and training outlines for both the building occupier and the engineering and maintenance personnel.

The service organisation must use this information and take an integrated or holistic approach in structuring the operation and maintenance function.

19.4.2 Training needs assessment

The training needs assessment is used to compile a comparative inventory of the knowledge base and skills possessed by an individual operative against a specified competency outline. The difference between the specified requirements and the actual measured ability is the training required.

The use and provision of job descriptions for each of the core competencies within a organisation identifies the:

- key responsibilities
- levels of authority
- duties and demarcations
- qualifications.

If these basic competencies are established for each post, a training matrix can be created for the core posts within the organisation and this can be used as a comparator to assess training requirements for specific jobs.

The establishment of a training matrix has the additional benefit of providing a basis for reviewing the existing structure and future restructuring of the service organisation and also provides an employee selection criteria. There is no financial case for employing staff who do not satisfy the criteria identified within the job description; to do so will only increase the overall training costs.

Additional training needs will be required to meet particular project and organisational requirements. These may include:

- professional and technical qualifications
- trade skills
- management skills
- specialist process skills
- understanding of health and safety procedures and legislation
- understanding of environmental issues
- understanding of facilities management.

Health and safety is a subject that has increased in significance in recent years, as have quality and risk management.

19.4.2.1 Health and safety

The subject of health and safety is a major element of staff training. The establishment of safe systems of work for all the operation and maintenance functions is a statutory requirement under the CDM Regulations(1) (see also section 18). Staff have to be trained to understand the requirements of the legislation that apply to the tasks they are required to carry out and to recognise the possible risks to health in carrying out those tasks. Risk assessment should identify the potential hazards, while implementation of safe systems of work should eliminate or reduce the risk.

Where the risk remains significant and the hazard cannot be eliminated, control measures need to be implemented. If the risk is life threatening, control measures should extend to more prescriptive arrangements such as permit-to-work procedures. Staff involved in these areas of work need to be trained specifically to meet that requirement and certified by the organisation as competent to carry out specified tasks.

There must also be a health and safety plan (an extension, in effect, of the construction phase health and safety plan) that will plan, action, monitor and review all health and safety activities on a regular and continuous basis. Information and training has to be provided to ensure that all concerned understand the need for the procedures and how they are to be applied.

19.4.2.2 Quality management

Customers have a continuously increasing expectation of service and performance. Engineering staff involved in the operating and maintenance of a modern building need to be provided with the appropriate skills in:

- customer awareness
- quality aims and objectives of the business
- quality management procedures
- performance criteria and measurement techniques
- individual responsibility for quality
- continuous improvement cycle.

19.4.2.3 Risk management

Those responsible for the management and operation of the maintenance function need to identify and understand the factors that represent the greatest risk to the continuity of the core business process. These should be formally documented and translated into procedures and work practices to eliminate such risks. The engineering management staff has to be trained to undertake the task of quantifying the risks and to prepare operation and maintenance working procedures that keep the risks to a minimum. The resulting information, understanding and working procedures then have to be conveyed to the operational staff.

19.5 Training plan

Training has a cost and this has to be accounted for financially. Each business unit or department within an organisation needs to identify:

- how the training will meet the business targets
- the resources that will be allocated
- the investment value within the annual business plan for the forthcoming financial year
- the method of measurement of the benefit achieved.

Training plans are subject to change. A process for the review of the training plan should be in place to ensure that:

- training is prioritised to meet the changing needs of the business
- actual commitment is made in accordance with the training plan
- training is delivered according to business or project needs
- any additional or new training requirements are identified and scheduled
- regular reviews of expenditure on training are undertaken.

Preview of the training activity is essential to ensure that training meets both the short and long-term targets, that training remains effective and that there is a continuing commitment from all levels of management.

19.6 Means of provision

Having assessed the training needs, the method and resources to deliver that training have to be identified. Training can be delivered through:

- universities
- further and higher education colleges
- independent training organisations
- internal courses utilising expertise available within the business or the original design team
- distance learning courses
- cross-training
- multi-media/interactive training products
- trade organisations and professional institutions
- equipment or product manufacturers
- seminars and conferences.

The choice of training method and provider will be based on the effectiveness and value for money required by the individual company. Where a business is centralised in one building, training is easier to deliver than in an organisation that has a number of offices spread over a large geographical area.

19.7 Environment

The training environment is a major factor in the effective delivery of training. Important elements affecting the effectiveness of training are:

- furniture comfort
- lighting levels, ventilation, temperature and humidity control
- quality and quantity of course material
- teaching equipment and facilities
- course tutors
- delegate class numbers
- a sympathy with and understanding of the requirements of individual delegates.

The effects of these elements are well understood by professional training organisations, but the same standards must be achieved in the delivery of any internal or site-based training. These, plus any additional personal variations, should be confirmed prior to any training commitment.

19.8 Certification

The certifying authority is an important issue in the selection of training courses, particularly where proof of competence is required. It is desirable that the certification is provided by a national or industry recognised authority.

Where there is no certifying authority, certification from other bodies may be accepted but should, generally, be restricted to:

- registered training organisations
- trade associations
- reputable manufacturers of plant or equipment relevant to the business.

19.9 Evaluation

Having provided the training, there needs to be evaluation to assess its effectiveness and to ensure that:

- skills acquired by the employee are adequate for the task or process to be carried out
- training has met the employeeís training need
- training has met the overall business aims and objectives.

It is essential to prove measurable benefit as a result of providing training. The criteria for demonstrating the actual cost effectiveness or operational benefit of the training should be detailed and set out when the training programme is still at the approval stage.

19.10 Records

Good training records are essential to prove the competence and development of each individual employee. Ideally, the records should be:

- easily accessible
- available at all times
- reviewed on a regular basis
- kept up to date.

The training records have another important and valuable use; that is to provide statistics on the training carried out by the organisation. For example:

- number of person days of training carried out in any one period
- types of training provided
- cost of training provided.

These statistics should be made available to employees and customers, and maximise the value of the training achievement.

References

1 *The Construction (Design and Management) Regulations 1994* Statutory Instrument 1994 No. 3140 (London: The Stationery Office) (1994)

2 *The Management of Health and Safety at Work Regulations 1992* Statutory Instrument 1992 No. 2051 (London: The Stationery Office) (1992)